Fetch It, Rusty!

From left to right: Charles Hill, the English setter Sam, A.D. Harrell, and the Brittany Rusty, with three grouse; Mitchell County, North Carolina. Photo by Charles Hill, using delayed exposures.

Fetch It, Rusty!

A.D. Harrell

Celo Valley Books
Burnsville, North Carolina

Copies of this book may be obtained by sending $20.00 plus $2.50 postage to the author (A.D. Harrell, Route 1, Box 276, Bakersville NC 28705), or by asking your local bookstore to order it either from the publisher or from their favorite wholesaler.

Library of Congress Catalog Card Number 96-85442

ISBN 0-923687-38-6

Printed in the United States of America.

Front cover photo: The author and Rusty with their grouse (photo by Charles Hill). Back cover photo: Geneva Harrell and her grouse: Wisconsin, 1991.

Unless otherwise noted in captions, all photos in text are by Harrell family members and friends.

CONTENTS

LIST OF ILLUSTRATIONS

FOREWORD

A man's thoughts are his own. His cares and problems subside as he follows the rutted path sunk deep in the terrain by logs snaked from the mountain top. With gun over his shoulder, his favorite dog at his side and a friend to keep him company, he pauses now and then to survey the submerged fields and streams below. A startled animal bounds away from the hunter, who puts his hand on the whining dog, smiles at his friend, and gives thanks for the beauty of God's world. This scene, so familiar to the writer, has inspired him to share this and other aspects of his life with the reader.

Fetch It, Rusty! by A.D. Harrell is a collection of short stories and sketches which reveal his innermost thoughts, values, and experiences. He is a naturalist, an avid sportsman, a valued neighbor, a community leader, and a devoted family man.

A.D. Harrell, son of Luther and Arizona Harrell, was born in the Harrell Hill community of Mitchell County. He was steeped in Christian traditions, in the value of hard work, and in the importance of education.

Since education has always been a top priority of the Harrell family, it is understandable that a variety of the stories are about education and related school activities. A.D., his five sisters, and one brother graduated from Appalachian State University at Boone, North Carolina. A.D. and his wife, Geneva, have four children. All of the children have university degrees, and one earned a Ph.D. from the University of North Carolina at Chapel Hill.

A.D. started his formal education at the age of three at Harrell Hill School. He completed high school at age sixteen and college at age nineteen. After a four-year period in the Navy during World War II, he spent twenty years as a high school teacher and athletic coach. In 1958, the staff of Tipton Hill High School dedicated the year book to him.

His concern for the welfare of the child was of paramount importance when he served as an elected member and chairman of the Mitchell County Board of Education. He received a certificate of appreciation for outstanding volunteer service from the North Carolina governor's office during his term as chairman.

The writer's observations of the surrounding topography and its habitat is the driving force behind his environmental activities. A man of action, he worked with other community leaders to bring about environmental awareness in Mitchell County. He was instrumental in leading the local movement to clean up the mining wastes from the Toe River. His efforts helped to promote a variety of recreational opportunities, including fishing for musky and small mouth bass. These environmental activities are related in his story, "Cleaning Up the Toe River."

A.D. served for ten years as director of the Mitchell County Soil Conservation District. He enthusiastically supported wildlife and fisheries management programs. Some of his activities in this regard are referred to in his hunting stories. The North Carolina Wildlife Resources Commission presented A.D. with their Gold District Conservation Award of Merit for contributions made toward conserving the valuable wildlife resources of North Carolina.

All of his environmental activities have not been away from home. Hard work and astute environmental practices resulted in the green, fertile hills of Harrell Hill Farm. On this farm he and his family operated a grade A dairy for twenty-one years. During this time, A.D. served as president of the Western North Carolina Dairy Producers.

Participation in community affairs has been a major part of the life of the writer. In 1958 he accepted a certificate of achievement for the Harrell Hill Community from the Asheville Agriculture Council. He has served as moderator of the congregation at the Pleasant Grove Church of the Brethren on Harrell Hill. A.D. chaired the committee which brought telephone service to the area west of Bakersville. He served twenty-six years as president of the Mitchell County Farm Bureau and played a vital role in upgrading the highway from Spruce Pine to Bakersville, which is related in one of the stories.

Hunting for wild game or casting for trout was always more enjoyable with a friend or family member. In his book, A.D. recalls episodes both serious and humorous about hunting with friends and family. For the past twenty years, he and his family have gone on hunting trips to Wisconsin.

Family comes first with A.D. His stories abound with incidents illustrating a high regard for his family. He has always found time for work and play with his children and grandchildren. His "Tribute to Geneva" is a delightful, sentimental story honoring his wife. A.D. and his Geneva have given their children a heritage in the Christian religion, a good education, and the value of hard work and responsibility.

Fetch It, Rusty! is a book to enjoy in its entirety or by selecting stories at random. The stories are told in the writer's distinctive style, with love and respect for all characters. The reader is left with appreciation for a man who sets and accomplishes exemplary goals for himself and his community.

Mae F. Fortner
1995

PREFACE

This book is about grouse hunting, hunting partners, and bird dogs. It is about some successful hunts and some notorious failures. It is also about some of the more mundane activities that a man must be engaged in if he is to keep body and soul together.

There is a subtle effort to record some of the history of my area, of my people, of the way life was in the 1920s, '30s, and '40s.

It is about a church that sits atop Harrell Hill.

It is about waiting for the frosty mornings of October—October, with its bright blue sky of Indian summer—and waiting for the opening of another grouse season.

I want to dedicate this book to my fine wife of fifty-two years, Geneva, and to our four fine children. These children in order of their birth are Douglas, Judy, Larry, and Rose Marie.

Without the ability, the intelligence, the dedication, and the love for family that Geneva has, my grouse hunts of the last forty years would never have taken place. Without her ability to supervise, to take care of whatever problem that might come up when I was away from home, we would not have had many of the pleasures we have enjoyed. Without her help and warm personality and many abilities, these four children of ours probably would not have been able to take university degrees. Each one has earned a bachelor's degree, and one has earned a Ph.D.

I hope I understand how lucky Geneva and I have been to have these four children, who are blessings in every respect. When once in a while I look around and see parents who are being sent to an early grave because of the continuous trouble their children have gotten into, I think this is especially true. Ours have been something to be proud of. And I give much of their success, not all of it of course, but much of it, to the fine mother they have had.

Editor's Note: A.D. Harrell has swapped stories with friends all of his life. It therefore seemed logical, when he decided to collect some of these stories in a book, to record them on tape and then transcribe the tapes. Because we used this technique, we consider this material to be a sort of oral history. Only minimal changes were made to the story text to increase clarity. The stories as presented here are organized around common themes, and thus the book sequence differs from the taped sequence.

The Brittany spaniel Rusty.

CHAPTER ONE

Tales and Advice
from the Grouse Woods

Playing Hookey to Hunt Grouse

When I taught in the local high school, the school day for me consisted of teaching math and social science and so forth. In the last period in the afternoon, my job was to coach the high school basketball team. That was the only duty I had that last period. On days that we had a game at night, I did not practice; I let the team rest and take it easy. So, frequently in that last period, I'd find some reason to slip off and get out of there and go home, get my bird dog and slip off to the woods.

On this particular day, I had a game that night and didn't have anything to tie me up the last period, so I figured I would go into the office and make up some lie, something to tell the principal to see if he wouldn't let me leave.

I went into the office. The principal had company. That company happened to be the superintendent of schools, Mr. Deyton.

"Well, I'm in here," I thought. "I might as well see if I can't get permission from both of them."

I came out with some such tale as this: I wasn't practicing basketball that period, and I didn't have any important assignments for the next hour and there were some things over at my house that needed my attention. They were of a nature that if I didn't give them my attention before the basketball game, they just wouldn't get my attention. That meant they needed my attention from something like three-thirty until I'd leave for the basketball game about six-thirty.

The principal asked the superintendent if he thought that would be all right.

Mr. Deyton said, "Yes, under the circumstances, if he has something important to do, I reckon that would be all right." So I got permission to leave.

It takes me eight minutes to drive from the schoolhouse to my house. I drove that eight minutes, rushed in my house, got my hunting togs on, got my gun, and got my bird dog. I drove out to a grouse hunting area, to a valley that a member of the board of education happened to own. Well, I parked my vehicle, got my dog, and walked up that valley. Before I got to the top of that valley, I had killed two grouse, so I started down the holler, back to my car.

Looking off down the valley aways, I saw what looked like a man coming up the valley. He looked a little unusual; I wasn't sure just what I was seeing.

Now, I've been out in the woods and I've seen all kinds of things. I've seen bootleggers, I've seen Canadian wolves, I've seen revenue officers, I've seen pure-T outlaws. But this was the first time that I had seen a man fully dressed in a business suit out in the grouse woods. Here was a man coming up that valley who had on a black business suit, a white shirt, a tie, and a white hat.

As the fellow came on up and I looked a little closer, I began to have some uneasy feelings. It looked like my boss. It looked like Mr. Deyton. It looked like the man that I had lied to within the last two hours so that I could get out into the woods to start with.

He came on up, and to my dismay, I saw that that was who it was. Well I knew without any doubt that I'd better say something appropriate. I'd better say something real wise, with real good judgment, something judicial, something that might get me out of what looked like a jam.

A.D. Harrell; Mitchell County, North Carolina, 1966. Photo by Joel Arrington, North Carolina Division of Travel and Tourism.

I thought through all those requirements for two or three seconds. Of course, I didn't have much time. I had an uneasy feeling, anyhow. I realized what a grouse felt like when it was trying to hide in the brush and a bird dog comes up and points it. I felt like I was *pointed*.

But it was time to say something. Although I knew what should be said, what I came out with was, "What in the hell are you doing here?"

In his slow, polite voice, Mr. Deyton said, "I need to have a board of education meeting tonight. I'm looking for Mr. Griffith (who was a member of the board of education), and I understand he is working up in this valley somewhere. I'm coming to get a message to him to try to attend the board meeting tonight. There is something important that I need to get worked out. Have you seen Mr. Griffith?"

"No. No, I haven't seen him."

I reached back in my game bag, where I had the two grouse that I had killed. "Here, I'd like you to have a grouse."

Mr. Deyton said, "No. Thank you. I wouldn't care for one. Wouldn't know what to do with it."

"Well, what you do with it is you take it home and clean it and dress it like you would a chicken and you have your wife cook it for you, then you eat it."

"Well, I wouldn't care for one anyway. Thank you." So he went on up the valley and I went down the valley.

I went down the valley shaking my head, saying to myself, "There are just some human beings who just haven't gotten tuned into the finer things of life." But I was glad to get out of there.

First Hunting Trip to Wisconsin

In 1956 I was engaged in an effort to develop plots out in the forest that would provide food for grouse in the bad winter months of January and February. Frequently in this area during those two months we have some winter snow up to three or four feet. I was making some effort to find plants that would provide food for grouse under those conditions—particularly plants that would give grouse cover from predators—and would hold their seeds or berries until April.

There aren't too many plants in this country that meet those qualifications. Most plants produce their fruit or berries in the fall of the year, in September or October, and they shed those fruits with the coming of the first heavy frost. There are a few plants, if you can find them, that carry their seeds over the winter.

In the search for those types of plants, I got in touch with the Wildlife Commission in Raleigh, told them what I was doing, and asked them for any technical or professional assistance that they might be able to give me. In response to my request, they sent me one of their biologists, a man named Charles Hill. Charles is a graduate of North Carolina State University in the field of wildlife biology. He was one of the most capable and most efficient men that they could have sent me.

He came to see me and we went over the project that I was attempting. He helped me with some plants and pointed out that the Wildlife Commission could help me get some autumn olive, some Japanese honeysuckle, some barberries, and some nandina. These plants flower heavily in the late fall and carry their berries and seeds throughout the winter. With the assistance of Charles Hill, I put out several successful food areas for grouse.

Through that contact, I made a friend of Charles Hill and I invited him in years to come to grouse hunt with me, which he did. Over the years we had several fine days of grouse hunting, several fine days of companionship. We hunted grouse together, we hunted ducks together, we hunted turkey together, and his wife and my wife got to be good friends. Charles Hill fulfilled all of the requirements that I have for a grouse hunting partner.

In 1972 after we had hunted together for several years, Charles invited Geneva and me to go with him and his wife, Anna Frances, to the northern part of Wisconsin to look at the grouse hunting possibilities there. On October the sixth or seventh, 1972, we left this area and drove to Wisconsin.

The drive from our place to northern Wisconsin is a two-day drive. On the last day of that drive, we really wanted to get to our destination in time to have an hour or two to take the dogs out and let them limber up and get some exercise, and to let us get in some hunting, too. By two or three o'clock in the afternoon, it was clear that we weren't going to be able to get to our destination in time to hunt before dark.

About four o'clock we made the decision to find a wide place on the side of the road and pull our vehicle off. It was agreed that Charles and I would take the two dogs out and go hunting while the ladies fixed some sandwiches. Where, we didn't know.

We found a wide place on the left side of the road and pulled the vehicle off. We got the two dogs out of their crates and turned them loose and hit the woods that came down right close to the road. We didn't know then, and I don't know to this day, whether that was private land or public land or state forest or county forest or what it was. But we took our chances and went into the woods with those two bird dogs and our two guns.

Just a little ways inside the woods, one of the dogs pointed, and the other moved up in back of him. Charles and I went in. One of us, I don't remember which one, maybe both of us, shot the bird and it fell. We repeated that episode maybe four or five times within the next forty-five minutes.

We came out in a clearing. Close to us was a farmhouse. We found that we were almost in the back door of somebody's house. We sneaked back into the woods and turned round and headed back to the vehicle. By the time we got back to that vehicle, we had been gone fifty minutes, probably, but we had killed five grouse. That's about as perfect a fifty minutes as a person can have.

I have never again been able to find that exact location, but later that day we ended up at a campground at Three Lakes, Wisconsin. It was Olson's campground.

We were there for two weeks and we hunted every day. We took two dogs, and the ladies hunted, too. We had two wonderful weeks hunting around Three Lakes, Eagle River, and Rhinelander in the counties of Oneida and Vilas, in Nicolet National Forest. We found plenty of grouse. I don't remember how many birds we killed, but we did kill some grouse and some woodcock. We did some duck hunting, too. We took a canoe on top of our vehicle, and we hunted some of the lakes in Wisconsin. We had a wonderful two weeks in northern Wisconsin.

With that beginning in 1972, we have hunted in northern Wisconsin each year. As the years went by, we broadened the party and took other family members. Charles took, in addition to his wife, their daughter. We began to take our two sons.

We still spend two weeks up there, from October the eighth to around October the twentieth. We have found from experience that you have to get out of that country and get your vehicles out by no later than October the twenty-first. We have been snowbound a time or two by as early as October the twentieth.

We have switched our first week of hunting to the Chequamegon National Forest, which is in northwestern Wisconsin. We stay in a little village named Glidden with some real good friends that we have made. Those friends are a man and wife by the name of Kubley, Carl and Jean Kubley. We haven't found anywhere finer people, more warmhearted hosts, more pleasant people than Carl and Jean. We have hunted the last eight years there, probably, for the first week of our trip, staying in the Kubley's facility, which is a campground of some six to eight individual cabins. After hunting there a week, we shift back over to the Three Lakes area and finish our hunting at that place.

Carl Kubley, owner of the cabin where the Harrells stay in Wisconsin, and his grouse.

It has come to be an annual affair for the Harrell family. We have some grandsons who are still too young to go along, but they are waiting with a lot of anxious moments until they are old enough to join us on the Wisconsin hunts. Of course, their granddaddy is looking forward to having them go along with us.

The Magic of a Good Name

When the farmers of my area started sowing on their cropland and on their pastureland a grass called fescue, the bobwhite quail population was reduced by around ninety-five percent. This happened because fescue is a vigorous growing and a dominant grass. It crowded out the small plants, such as lespedeza, that produced the seed that the quail lived on. Since we had so few quail in the 1960s, I started doing some quail hunting in Polk County, in the Piedmont, near the South Carolina line. Polk County is the home county of my wife, Geneva.

One fine December morning, I picked up Ed Terrell, our agricultural chairman, and took him with me quail hunting in Polk County. We started hunting on Mr. Ray Horne's farm, Geneva's brother's farm, and were lucky enough to find birds immediately. My dog pointed the covey, and we killed two or three birds on the first rise.

The remainder of the covey flew across the highway and settled down in a field east of the road. I knew that property belonged to someone other than Mr. Horne. Since we saw no posters, we crawled over the fence on the west side of the highway, walked across the road, and crawled over the fence on the east side of the highway, into the field where the quail had lit.

Right quick the dog pointed quail and we started shooting. This went on for some twenty minutes. We were killing some birds.

The dog pointed another time. As we approached the dog, we could see a man coming across the field, toward us. Even at one hundred yards, we could tell that the gentleman was angry. We couldn't tell how angry, but from the way he was putting his feet down it was clear he was somewhat steamed up.

We walked on past the pointing dog, just left it on point. We walked a few steps toward the gentleman and waited for him to come on up. At that stage we could see that his face was red with anger. His jaw was set in a hard, straight line. His lips were pressed together so tight they were white. He was wearing a knee-length black overcoat, and each hand was pressed down into the pockets of that big coat.

It occurred to me that if I started talking before he started cussing, I might calm him down.

"I'm A.D. Harrell," I said. "This is Ed Terrell. We were invited by Mr. Horne to hunt on his property across the road. When the birds flushed, they came across the road, over here, and we followed them. I married a girl from this community, and that is how I come to have permission from Mr. Ray Horne."

"Who did you marry?"

"Geneva Horne. One of Jess Horne's daughters."

The anger left the man's face. He took his hands out of this pockets. He shook his head gently and smiled.

"Geneva Horne was one of my classmates," he said. "She was one of the best friends I ever had. We weren't sweethearts or anything like that, just real good friends. She helped me with math, with algebra and geometry. Without her help, I might not have got through high school. My name is Harold Weaver. Since you married Geneva, you are welcome to hunt here today. If you want to come back for another day sometime later on, you'll be welcome. Just tell Geneva I said 'hello.'"

Benefits of Grouse Hunting

There are many people that I know that when they feel a cold coming on, a headache or something, or tension kind of getting them down, take an aspirin or Stanback, or whatever they happen to have, and go to bed and rest awhile and try to wear it off. That's well and good, but I haven't found that effective in my case. When I get uptight with pressures of work and this 'n that, or when I'm taking a cold, or when I'm just feeling under the weather, I've found that if I get my gun and bird dog and drive out to the grouse woods and take off up one side of these mountains I'll immediately relieve the tension and any pressures that I might have. I've found out that if I walk fast enough and hard enough and long enough to get up a sweat, to get the perspiration to flowing, get the heart to beating heavy, get the blood to pumping, that that's about all I need to cure a cold. That's worked for me probably some five hundred times. I don't think it has ever failed.

Now, if I have a sore throat and a temperature, that's a different situation. But if I'm just taking a cold, or tension or something is getting me down, then a good hunt with a bird dog with some real strong, vigorous exercise, that's all I need. Hunting has stood me in good stead for years and years and years, and I have habitually used that hunting to relieve pressure.

I have noticed on the part of our older son, that when he comes in from working his job and is worn out and flustered and needing some recreation, all he has to do is get out with his daddy and he forgets all that stuff, gets it all out of his mind, and he relaxes and starts feeling better immediately.

Now I catalog that relieving tension as one of the values of hunting, but not all of the value of hunting. Exercise involved in the walking and climbing around is real good to keep your blood pressure down. It's real good to keep the arteries open and the heart functioning well, to keep the heart healthy, and to keep all muscles in tone. I think the medical profession agrees that a certain amount of vigorous walking two or three times a week or so is probably the best exercise the human body can take.

Hunting for me substitutes for medicine. Some years ago I went to an eye hospital to have a cataract removed and a lens implanted. They asked me a hundred questions, it seemed like. One of the questions that both the nurse and the doctor asked me was, "Mr. Harrell, what kind of medicine are you taking?"

I said to the doctor, "Sir, I'm not taking any medicine."

"How long has it been since you took any medicine?"

"It's probably been, oh, three or four years."

The doctor straightened up and said, "Well, I've been in this business some time, fifteen years, and you are the first patient that I have ever had who wasn't taking any medicine or hadn't taken any medicine in the last six months."

"Doctor, I can tell you the reason for it, if you want to know why. It's climbing those mountains, going up and down those hills, and shooting grouse."

He laughed and said, "I've shot a grouse or two in my life. I'm from Minnesota and I know what you're talking about."

There are many, many, many values to hunting in the out-of-doors, and I have received many blessings from these values. We as a family have at every opportunity taken our boys and girls to the out-of-doors, especially on the weekends and holidays. That gets them away from the highways, that gets them away from fast automobiles, that gets them away from possible drugs, that gets them away from possible alcohol, that gets them away from people or companions that might get them in difficulty or in trouble. We take them out where it's clean and wholesome, with wholesome company, and teach them to enjoy being outdoors, and they thoroughly enjoy that experience. And it could just be that we've not had any trouble from our boys or girls because in the years that they were more susceptible to getting off on the wrong foot, much of that time was taken up with their daddy, out with the dogs, hunting and having a good time.

This point is underscored by John Parris in his "Roaming the Mountains" column in the *Asheville Citizen-Times* (Monday, November 27, 1995) with a quote from Supreme Court Justice William O. Douglas, who was a mountain climber. Parris quotes Douglas as saying:

Grandfather A.D. Harrell, son Doug, and grandson Tony, at the end of a successful day in Wisconsin in 1992.

Mountains have a decent influence on men. . . . I have never met along the trails of the high mountains a mean man, a man who would cheat and steal. . . . When a man ventures into the wilderness, climbs the ridges, and sleeps in the forest, he comes in close communion with his Creator.

When man pits himself against the mountains, he taps inner springs of his strength. He comes to know himself.

. . . The woods are a good place for man or boy to shout and yell. Everyone accumulates steam that is hard to blow off. There is nothing quite so good for that ailment as a lusty bellow at the top of a mountain ridge or at the base of a towering cliff.

Besides, there is no neighbor to be disturbed. There is no sensitive or fidgety person who might translate such sound into either a breach of the peace or a sign of approaching insanity. . . . It is better that a lad face adventure on a stream or lake than risk the more subtle dangers of the poolroom. The streams and lakes do not breed juvenile delinquents.

I would recommend to any father with sons, that if it is available to him, get those sons off the street, get them out of the drug store, get them out of the pool room, get them away from the race track, and take 'em hunting, take 'em fishing. Get them out and get them some exercise and teach them that there are better things than what you run into in the urban areas.

Gabriel's Trumpet

You wouldn't normally think that grouse hunting would have anything to do with Gabriel and his trumpet and the coming of the Biblical end of time. But on one of my grouse hunts, there was a real close association between the two in the mind of one young man.

Now, grouse hunting is a little more enjoyable if you have company with you, someone to talk to, someone to laugh with if you miss, someone to brag to if you do good, and someone to point out what a fine dog you have. Just a lot of reasons for having company. So, on most of my grouse hunts I try to find a good fellow to go with me.

I do put some restrictions on whom I take. My grouse hunting partners have to be people who don't use alcohol to any excess. They have to be people who don't engage in foul, vulgar language. They have to be enjoyable to be with. A good neighbor of mine, Mr. Hobart Miller, fit all these categories, and years ago I invited him to accompany me on a grouse hunt on a Saturday.

We drove into the hunting area and decided to separate temporarily and to meet later on in the morning. Mr. Miller went up one valley that leads to the top of a mountain, and I went up another valley that ends up at the top of the same mountain. Before we separated, we agreed on certain signals to exchange so we could find each other. And we agreed that I would find Mr. Miller, not Mr. Miller find me, which meant that when those signals were exchanged, Mr. Miller was to sit down where he was and I was to go hunting him.

The signals consisted of this: When I got to the top of the mountain where we were going to meet, I was to blow in my gun barrel. If Mr. Miller was up there and heard me, he would count one . . . , two . . . , three . . . , then he would shoot. I'd wait half a minute after he shot, then I'd blow on that gun barrel two more times.

Now if you don't know about guns, you'd need some explanation here. To blow in a gun barrel, you take the shell out of the gun, turn the barrel around, and put to your mouth the end of the barrel the shot comes out of when you shoot. And you pucker up your lips and you blow on that gun barrel just as if you were blowing on a bugle. After a little practice, you will be amazed at how much sound, how much volume, you can get and how far that volume will carry out in the woods.

After we exchanged signals, I found Mr. Miller sitting on a stump beside of what we call a drag trail, an old abandoned logging road where in years past loggers with teams of horses have pulled logs down to a loading area. I asked Mr. Miller how he got along on the trip. Had he seen anything? He said that, no, he hadn't shot.

"I didn't see anything but a man," he said. "Have you seen a man?"

"No. No, I didn't see any man."

"Well, the darndest thing happened. I was sitting on this stump here, perfectly still, right beside this trail, and you blew the gun barrel. Just a little while after you blew the gun barrel, here comes down this log trail a man running at a full gallop, as hard as he could run. I was afraid he was going to break his neck and kill himself, he was running so fast down that rough road. He ran right down by me. I could have touched him with my hand almost, but he didn't see me. Before he got out of sight, he laid down in the trail, took his hands and pulled leaves all over his legs, all over his body, all over his face, and covered himself up. I wondered if I was seeing things, if I'd lost it all. I had never seen anything like that.

"I sat there, staring in amazement at that pile of leaves down there that that man had piled on top of himself. About then, you blew the other two times on the gun barrel, as we had agreed you would do. When you blew those notes, those leaves exploded and that man came out of there and went out of sight, jumping as far as he could jump right down the side of the mountain. I've never seen anything like it in my life. Man didn't have a gun, but he was flying. Appeared to be scared to death."

I said I had no idea of what was going on. "But I know people all over this area, and he would certainly be from some family in the general area. Next week in school, I'll ask and I'll see if I can't find out who that was."

The following Monday, during the basketball practice, when I was letting the team take a time out and rest, sitting on the bleachers, I recounted part of this story. Nobody said a word. They just listened, their eyes wide open in amazement, but nobody spoke.

After school that afternoon, a young lady came to me and said, "Mr. Harrell, that was my brother, Lee. He got scared to death out there in the mountains."

"Well, I'll talk with Lee," I said, so the next time I ran into Lee at school, I mentioned it to him.

"I'll tell you now, I got really shook up," said Lee. He was about fourteen years old, but a real big boy, probably about six foot one or two.

"I had decided to go deer hunting that Saturday morning, so I went out on that mountain. I had never been so far from home in the mountains by myself, and I was nervous from that standpoint. And I was nervous from some other standpoints, too. I was deer hunting, but the deer season wasn't open, so I was breaking the law. I was not only far enough away from home to be scared, I was also scared the game warden was going to get me. So I was just nervous.

"I was sitting there real quiet, watching for a deer. You could have heard a pin drop. I hadn't heard or seen one thing on earth. It was quiet as could be. All of a sudden here sounded this trumpet up there on top of the mountain. It wasn't a small sound. It made my ears ring.

"The first thing I thought of is, 'Lord have mercy, that's Gabriel. The end of time is coming and he's blowing his horn to tell us. I don't want to die out here on this mountain by myself. I want to get to my family.' So, I threw my gun away and I took off down that mountain as hard as I could run.

"I got a little bit tired and I thought, 'It's two miles home. I'll never make it. I'll never get there. I'll just lay down here and cover myself up. Maybe it will all blow over and I'll be all right.' So, I laid there in the leaves and I covered myself up completely.

"I laid there in those leaves almost shaking. But still, I was covered up and I felt a little bit of safety from being covered up. About that time, Gabriel blew that trumpet again, and in a second he blew it again. I said, 'Lord have mercy, he has seen me. They've found me. I am going home.'

"I came out of those leaves, and it took me about thirty minutes to run home, but I got home. I've never been that scared in my life. I don't ever expect to be that scared again."

I told Lee what had happened, and he said, "Well, that's something. But it really shook me."

Mr. Miller has long passed away, but Lee is still living. We run into each other once in a while. Sometimes, over at the store, I'll stop and buy him a drink, and we'll go out on the loafers' bench and we'll talk about Gabriel's trumpet.

Hunting Safety and Etiquette

In all hunting trips there are two major concerns that in my opinion should always receive a major priority. Number one of these two is safety. Number two is consideration for the happiness or the enthusiasm of your guest. I will speak to the safety part first.

We never load a gun until we're on the ground, out of the vehicle, ready to walk in the woods. This means no loaded gun in a vehicle at any time. When we're actually hunting, guns are always to be pointed in some direction, or carried so they are pointed in some direction, away from your partner and away from your dog.

When we come to a fence or an obstruction of any kind that requires major interest in negotiating or crossing, the policy is for one person to walk up to the fence and turn around and hand his gun to his buddy. Then, the man with no gun gets on the other side. When he is safely on the other side, he reaches over and takes both guns from the other man.

For this exchange, the guns should be unloaded. After both men are across, we can reload and go on about our business.

In negotiating dangerous terrain—slick snow, or ice, or once in a while, walking a log in the woods—we also unload the guns. When we're over the dangerous spot, we reload.

Regardless of what kind of target presents itself, regardless of how many birds might flush, regardless of what the situation is, never fire that gun unless you can see that partner. For that reason, I have refused to hunt with three people in a party. It's just simply too difficult to know at all times where both the other two men are. With just two men in a party, it's fairly simple to know where the other man is. If there are three men, it gets real difficult.

Nothing is so important in hunting as safety. To my pleasure, I have noted that our two sons have made part of their hunting and part of their philosophy, I think unconsciously so now, the very things that I have noted here. They do everything possible to make hunting safe and they never make an unsafe movement.

Another thing I've stressed in grouse hunting in relation to safety is that the happiness of your partner should be the number one thing in your mind for the entire day. Always put that partner out in front of you. Always give him the advantage. If a dog points, give that partner the best position. If you are walking in an area where it's necessary to walk single file, always have that partner walk in front. Never take a shot that your partner could take. Make every decision along the line of seeing to it that your partner has a good time, that he is enjoying himself, that he is presented with all opportunities there happen to be.

Time and time again grouse hunters hunting together may shoot at the same bird at the same time. I have made it a policy (and my two sons adhere to the same policy) that if I shoot at the same time my partner does and the bird falls, and my partner turns around and says, "Did you shoot?" I say, "No, I didn't shoot."

If I can't lie out of it, and he knows that I did shoot, I say, "Well, my angle of shot was so bad that I couldn't possibly have hit that bird; it must be your bird." There isn't a situation that dictates anything other than helping your partner have a good time. The purpose of the whole trip is putting that partner out in front and seeing to it that he enjoys himself.

It is my belief that these points, the one on safety and the one about your partner having a good time, are the basic foundation of all outdoor activities. Observing these points will make a pleasant day for everyone.

First Meeting with Big John

One day in 1965 there was a KNOCK-KNOCK-KNOCK on the door of the room where I was teaching a high school math class. On opening the door, I saw a personable young man. I guessed his age to be in the mid-twenties. He was dressed in olive green pants and a gray shirt with a metal name plate, all of which indicated he was from the North Carolina Wildlife Resources Commission.

He stuck out his hand and with a big friendly grin said, "You're Mr. Harrell?"

"Yes. I am."

"My name is Big John and Clyde Patton sent me up here to see what you wanted and to help you in any way that I could."

"It's near lunch time. Let me finish my math class, and we'll have lunch together and have time to talk about anything we need to discuss."

Clyde Patton was the executive secretary of the Wildlife Resources Commission. Sometime earlier, I had written his department a letter, requesting assistance in reestablishing a bob white quail population in Mitchell County. We had just come through a severe winter, with snow depths of eight to ten inches over a period of six consecutive weeks. It was my judgment that no bobwhite quail could survive in these mountains with that much snow over that period of time.

Of course, "Big John" was not my visitor's name, but it's close enough.

After I finished my math class, we had lunch together and discussed the quail situation. Among other things, I found out that Big John was originally from Elkin, North Carolina, and that he had recently graduated from North Carolina State University, in wildlife biology. Upon graduation, he had secured employment with the North Carolina Wildlife Resources Commission.

A.D., Big John, and Charles Hill taking a lunch break from grouse hunting; Mitchell County, North Carolina, 1966. Photo by Joel Arrington, North Carolina Division of Travel and Tourism.

At that time, the North Carolina Wildlife Resources Commission was supported almost entirely by the revenue that came in from the purchase of fishing and hunting licenses by the sportsmen of the state of North Carolina. Some federal funds came in from what was known as the Pittman-Robertson Act, which gave some excise tax money on hunting and fishing equipment back to the states in which the purchases were made. In later years, there got to be some money for that commission appropriated by the North Carolina General Assembly, but that's beside the story here.

I made friends with Big John. He was a real likeable fellow, a real pleasant person, and I invited him to come to my place and let me introduce him to grouse hunting. He took me up on the offer.

Big John came to my house many times, and we hunted grouse in the Pisgah National Forest. We hunted a twenty-eight thousand acre area that had burned over in the 1940s. When we were hunting in the '60s and '70s, the burned over area was in the process of regeneration, or renewal, of the vegetation, and it offered excellent grouse habitat. It has been my experience over the years that if you can hunt an area that has been burned over eight to ten or twelve years previously, and it's in the grouse range, you will likely find ruffed grouse.

Frequently, we would have forty to fifty flushes in a day's hunt. Those hunts usually started around ten o'clock and lasted until about dark. I had an excellent grouse dog at the time, a pointer named Spot. With her help we killed many, many birds. The limit in North Carolina was then and is now three birds per day, per hunter. We were usually lucky enough to get the limit.

An Early Grouse Hunt

I started ruffed grouse hunting at the tender age of nine or ten, or somewhere along in there, around 1927 or '28. I hunted for probably three or four years before I killed a grouse. I didn't have a dog to help me and the gun I was using was not made for grouse hunting; it was made for squirrel hunting. The gun had a full choke barrel, which shoots a real tight pattern out there at twenty or thirty yards. These guns are satisfactory for shooting at stationary targets, but not for birds flying through the brush at a fast speed. For years I didn't kill a bird, as I wasn't lucky enough to find one sitting on the ground.

One morning when there was about four or five inches of snow on the ground, I walked from my house through the snow for about a mile and a half into an area where I had seen birds in the past. Sure enough, there were birds there. Four or five flushed and flew away, but I didn't shoot at them. Then another one flushed. Instead of flying away, it flew about ten or twelve yards and lit on the ground, in the snow, about fifteen yards away.

I thought, "Finally, I've got one! I just can't miss one that close to me, sitting still."

I raised my gun and took very careful aim to be sure I wouldn't miss that bird, and I squeezed the trigger. Instead of going **KABOOM** and killing the bird, it went SPAT, and the grouse flew away.

I had forgotten to put a shell in the gun barrel, so eager was I to get out to the woods, so that when I pulled the trigger the gun made that little SPAT noise. I loaded my gun and walked back the mile and a half through the snow. Still no grouse, but determined that next time I would load that gun.

The Triple

In 1966 a young man named Frank Bennett came to me and said, "A.D., I know where some grouse are down at my dad's. I want you to come down there and bring your dog some Saturday. I want to go with you. I've never seen a bird dog work, and I want to go with you and watch your bird dog work and watch you shoot grouse."

Frank Bennett had worked for me on the farm for some years, which was how we came to know each other. Frank grew up in the Poplar area, one of several boys in a big family, and Frank had a pretty hard time coming up. He had to work hard and so forth. He worked for me, as I said, and he went on to school, and eventually I let him have some land to put a trailer on.

Frank is one of my very best friends, a friend that I appreciate a lot because I've known him since he was three or four years old.

I went down to Frank's dad's to go grouse hunting. Frank and I took off across the mountain behind the house and came down on the other side of the mountain. My bird dog pointed about a hundred yards on down below us. Frank had a gun and of course I had a gun. I walked down to within fifteen or twenty yards of the dog. Frank wasn't right with me, and I looked back. He had stopped and was standing up on top of a stump. I said, "Come on. Let us go and you shoot, too."

He said, "No. I don't want to shoot. I just want to stand here and watch you. I want to see what happens."

I left Frank standing on the stump and took a few more steps to where the dog was. Grouse came up, a whole covey of grouse. I don't know how many there were, but I would say six to eight.

I started shooting. I stood right there in my tracks and shot at three grouse. I shot first at the one on the right of the group, and that bird fell. I pulled my gun barrel on around to the rest of them and fired again and another bird fell. I pulled my gun barrel a little farther around, fired again, and another bird fell.

Now, I had hunted grouse for years and years, probably for about twenty-five, at that time, and that's the first time in all those grouse hunting years that I got three grouse with me standing in the same place. It's called a triple.

When birds flush and you shoot twice and get two birds from that one flush, it's called a double. When you shoot three times at one flush and get three birds, it's called a triple. It doesn't go any further than that. There's no such thing as a quadruple.

Now I'm not really that good, but that one time I got a triple. I turned around to Frank.

He said, "Well I'm an S-O-B. You didn't miss a one of them. My brother thinks he can shoot. But he can't shoot. He doesn't know what he's doing, hardly."

An interesting addition to that episode. I mentioned that was the first time in twenty-five years that I got a triple. The following Tuesday (it was on a Saturday that I was out with Frank) I went out by myself, just the dog and me. The dog pointed. I was standing in a log road, clear territory, no heavy brush, when the dog pointed. I walked up to the dog, and lo and behold, three grouse flushed. I had a perfect opportunity to kill those three birds. I killed the first one, moved the barrel around and missed the second one, then killed the third one. I got two out of three. I had a perfect chance to get a triple, but I didn't.

That was 1960 something, and this is 1994. I am still grouse hunting, but I've never killed another triple and I don't expect to. A triple is just something unusual. For example, I know about this incident. Three men in the state of Pennsylvania spent their adult years grouse hunting. Near the end of their hunting years, one of them got a triple. The winter after he killed those three birds on one flush, the man passed away. The next summer, his two buddies got a truck, a bag of cement, and some sand and some rocks and went back in the forest where their buddy killed the triple. There they built a little monument out of rocks and cement. In that monument they embedded a plaque. That plaque says, in effect, that our buddy So-and-so (and they gave his full name) on such-and-such a date (and they gave the date) got a triple on grouse in this spot.

Hunting with Phil Dale

One night after I went to bed, probably about nine-thirty or ten o'clock, the telephone rang. It was a long distance call from a friend of mine named Phil Dale.

Phil said, "A.D., let's go grouse hunting tomorrow."

"Fine. It suits me. What time do you want to go?"

"About nine o'clock."

"Good. I'll be ready. Phil, where are you?"

"I'm in Inman, South Carolina. But I'll be there. It'll take me four hours, but I'll be there."

At nine o'clock the next day, Phil drove up. We visited with Geneva a little bit and had a cup of coffee. Then, I got my dogs and we took off.

During the night it had snowed a soft snow. By soft snow, I mean a snow that hangs on every limb, every blade of grass, every tree—everything. No wind. The snow is just there. If you touch those limbs, the snow falls off.

We hunted through the woods in that type of snow for about two hours. Of course, snow fell down our shirt collars, onto our bare necks. Snow fell into our pockets. Snow went into our shoes. Our shells had snow on them. To put shells in the guns, we had to wipe the snow off. But we were having a ball we thought.

After about two hours we sat down on a log to rest awhile. We ate sandwiches and talked about what a beautiful snow it was and this 'n that. Then things got real quiet. It was clear we were doing some serious thinking.

Phil turned around and looked at me and said, "A.D., you know, if we didn't like to do this, we'd be damned foolish to be out here."

"Amen."

Hunting an Outdoor Writer

On numerous occasions I've had requests to take outdoor writers on grouse hunts, so they can go back and write a story on grouse hunting for their respective magazines or newspapers. Usually these requests don't come directly to me. They most frequently are made first to the North Carolina Wildlife Commission from some magazine or newspaper wanting our commissioners to help their writer get in on a grouse hunt. The Wildlife Commission then frequently calls me, asking if I will assist such and such a writer and take him grouse hunting.

I have taken writers hunting on numerous occasions. I have taken writers from *Outdoor Life* and *Sports Afield*. I have taken a camera crew from the North Carolina Division of Travel and Tourism out for three days so they could film me and my partner and our dogs grouse hunting. The Wildlife Commission and the Division of Travel and Tourism made a TV tape and pictures and gave the schools around here a copy. The Bakersville Lions Club used that film for one of their programs.

I remember one particular situation when I took a man on a grouse hunt. A newspaper editor from Columbia, South Carolina (he was editor of the daily paper for Columbia) called on our Wildlife Commission and asked if they would find somebody to take their man on a grouse hunt so he could write a story about it. I agreed, after being contacted, to take the man.

He came to my place with two friends that I had hunted with over the years, Big John and Charles Hill. When we left to go hunting, the sky was fairly clear and the weather looked good. But later on, as the morning progressed, the clouds came in and the weather began to be very threatening.

About ten o'clock we separated into two parties: Charles and myself, and John and the writer. We agreed that at lunchtime we would meet on top of a mountain near an area called the Devil's Nest and have lunch. We pinpointed the particular location where we would meet.

By eleven o'clock it was snowing so hard that you could barely see to walk, so Charles and I didn't go to the appointed place. We hung out down in the valley, found a tree that we could get under, a huge hemlock, and we built a bonfire. We sat by that bonfire thinking the men in the other party, particularly John, would realize we would never climb that mountain in a snow storm and they would come down in the valley and eventually find us.

They did eventually come back, and my friend Big John told this story:

"When the snow storm hit, they were on the ridge line. It was snowing so hard that they could barely see. He said to the writer, "Now you sit on this log right here and while you're sitting on this log, you face west. Don't you move, don't you get up and take a step, don't you even turn around on this log and look east. You sit right on this log, facing in a western direction. When I come back, if you're sitting facing west, I'll find you. I've got to go out here to where we promised to meet Charles and A.D. and see if they're there. I don't think they will be there, but I have to go check. It'll take me thirty minutes to go out there and come back to you, so you sit right here on this log, and when I come back, I'll find you. I'll certainly find you if you're sitting right where you are this instant and if you're facing west.

"If you get up and turn around on this log and face east, I might not find you, it's snowing so hard. I'm telling you right now, if I don't find you, I'm not coming back to look for you in the morning. I'll wait till spring comes, then come back and see what we can find."

With that, Big John took off to the Devil's Nest to see if Charles and A.D. are there. Of course, we weren't there. Some thirty minutes later, John came back to the log. The writer was sitting just exactly where he left him. John tapped him on the shoulder and said, "Get up now, let's go."

The man stood up and there on the log was a dark place in the shape of his body where he had been sitting. Around it was about four inches of snow, which had fallen while John was gone.

They came on down the mountain and found Charles and me. Then, we sat there, warmed by that bonfire, and ate our lunch.

The writer went back to South Carolina and wrote that article for the newspaper. He sent me a copy of it. As I recall it, that writer said in his article, "I sat on that log, in the snow and prayed, 'Lord, if you will get me safely back to South Carolina, I'll never go grouse hunting again.'"

He also said something to the effect that, "You may think you want to go grouse hunting, but you really may not know if you want to go or not. Unless your muscles are in a finely toned situation, such as a super athlete, and unless the circulatory system is wide open and unless your heart can pump like a jackhammer, you ought to do something else rather than to go grouse hunting. I'd recommend that unless you qualify on all these points about muscles and heart and circulation that you consider maybe wrestling alligators or bears and let the grouse hunting go to someone who is in a little better shape than you might be in."

We wore that man out, really. He wasn't prepared for going up and down the hills that we hunt. In one paragraph in his article, he referred to some of my comments; I guess they were localisms. One of my frequent comments going up a valley was, "Let's drop over this hill here, because on the other side of this hill here I saw a grouse last week." He said that some time he wanted me to explain to him what I mean by that comment. "Dropping over the hill" means climbing a slope of about seventy-five degrees for a hundred and fifty yards, then kind of sliding down the other side.

In speaking of that writer's getting so tired and worn out, two
other instances come to mind. One is relative to Mr. Hobart Miller
that I spoke of in an earlier segment, the one about Gabriel's trumpet. The story goes that the next morning, Mr. Miller and his wife
were having breakfast together, just the two of them. Their children were grown at that time and had left home.

Mrs. Miller looked across to her husband, and asked, "Are you
going grouse hunting with A.D. today?"

Mr. Miller's answer was, "No. I'm not going today. I'm going to
dig some ditches and see if I can't rest a little bit."

Every now and again at a local country store I run into a friend
named Ed Tipton. I said to him once, "Ed, I want to ask a favor of
you."

He said all right.

I said, "Would you give me permission to park my truck, my
hunting vehicle, in your driveway or beside your driveway, or
there close to your house and leave it for four or five hours while I
go up in the back country to hunt grouse?"

"That will be fine. You can leave that truck anywhere you want
to and you can leave it just as long as you want to, under one condition. That condition is that you don't ask me to go with you!"

Hunting with John Lock

When our son Larry finished college, he went with the federal
government as a special agent in federal law enforcement. He was
sent to Newnan, Georgia, where he spent a few years working.

Larry called one night and said, "Daddy, I have a friend, John Lock, who wants me to bring him up there, and you and I take him grouse hunting. Could we work it out?"

I said, "Yea, we'll work it out. Bring him up here some Friday night or Saturday morning, and we'll go grouse hunting."

Over a period of two or three weeks, we made the plans and set up that particular grouse hunt. In the exchange of telephone calls back and forth to Newnan to set everything up, I asked some questions about John Lock's ability to climb these mountains and grouse hunt.

"Larry, how much exercise does John Lock get?"

"Well, he gets some exercise. He drinks at least one can of beer a day," Larry said and kind of laughed.

"Well now, you know how hard grouse hunting is. You go to John Lock and tell him that he'd better spend some days playing tennis or he'd better spend some days running a mile or two. He'd best spend some days getting some tough exercise of some kind or he won't be able to make this grouse hunt."

"I'll tell him."

Some week or so later, before they came up here, I had a chance to talk with John Lock.

"John, did Larry tell you what I said about getting some exercise?" "Yes. He told me."

"What did you do about it?"

"I didn't do much of anything about it, but I will get some exercise."

When the time come for them to get here, they drove up into the driveway. I stood at the picture window and looked down the driveway. I saw Larry get out of the vehicle and I saw John Lock get out of the vehicle. I watched John Lock walk the ten or fifteen steps up toward the door and I turned to my wife.

"Geneva, John Lock will never make a grouse hunter. He just won't be able to climb up and down these mountains, I don't think."

I thought John weighed about two-hundred-ten or -fifteen pounds, and he was about five foot nine or ten, probably, and didn't show the rigors of any strong exercise that I could tell.

They came on in. John was a real fine, pleasant young man. He was all excited, just bounding with energy to get out and go grouse hunting.

He and Larry and I drove up to the base of a mountain as far as we could drive. We got there about ten o'clock. We parked the vehicle and took off up the side of that mountain.

We walked for about an hour, stopping every little bit. I was very careful to watch John Lock to see how he was making it. He was doing pretty well. He was puffing a little, but not a great deal, and I stopped every fifteen minutes or so to let him rest.

We finally topped out at the ridge line and immediately ran into grouse. Each of us killed a bird or two. We headed south down that ridge line and hunted for another two hours.

By the time three hours had passed, John Lock had killed two grouse, believe it or not, and Larry had killed two grouse, and I had killed two grouse. I kept my eye on John to see how he was doing. He was doing fairly well, but he was showing little signs of being tired.

"Boys," I said, "we'd better turn off here, now, and head back toward the truck. It's about two miles to that truck, but it's down hill all the way. We've had a big day. I think we're all kind of tired and we'd better get on back to the truck."

We started back down that mountain.

John said, "I need to sit down and rest a little." So, we sat down and rested some.

It was clear that Mr. Lock was absolutely exhausted. I suggested that I take his game bag, which had his grouse and what was left of his lunch, and that Larry carry his gun. John Lock didn't have any disagreement with that. He thought that was a pretty good idea, so I took his bag and Larry took his gun and we started down the mountain.

The farther we got, the tireder John got, so we stopped and sat down again and rested awhile.

That time, I suggested that I take a knife and cut two walking sticks and let John Lock have one walking stick in each hand to help him get down the mountain. John didn't object to that at all, so we fixed him two big walking sticks.

After another hour, we finally got John Lock to the truck.

I haven't had in all of my grouse hunting years of experience a man who was any more exhausted than that fellow was. In fact, I know now that we were real lucky to get him back to the truck and get him in there and get him to sit down before he just absolutely gave out or had a heart attack on us.

Twenty-Six to Nothing

In its Division of Forestry, the state of North Carolina has a position know as the Extension Forester. The job of that Extension Forestry man is to coordinate forestry programs and efforts involving 4-H clubs, Future Farmers of America clubs, and extension services in the one hundred counties of North Carolina, all of it aiming toward better forestry practices in this state. In 1965 the man in that office was Mr. Ed Jones. Ed was a graduate of the forestry school at North Carolina State University. After graduation, Ed went to work for the North Carolina Forestry Extension Service and gradually worked himself up to be head of that whole department. In 1965, I don't know how it happened now, but some way Ed got invited by me to go on a grouse hunt. I don't remember the background of that, but Ed came up here.

Ed lived in Tarboro, North Carolina, which is in Edgecombe County. To come up here and grouse hunt a day means an overnight trip. Ed came up here a day early, spent the night with Geneva and me, and the next morning he and I went grouse hunting.

During our evening meal the night before we went hunting, at breakfast in the morning, and just during our general conversation, Ed was telling us how much experience he had in bird hunting. He kept bird dogs on his wife's farm in Tarboro. He quail hunted. He had done a lot of quail hunting.

He was raised in western North Carolina, in North Ridge. And being from western North Carolina, he knew something about grouse hunting. Although Ed had quail hunted for years and years and years, he wanted to go grouse hunting with me.

I've hunted with a few men who carry the most expensive gun, probably the most efficient gun, that you can buy. It's an over-and-under gun made by the Browning Corporation. I have never felt that I was wealthy enough to afford an over-and-under Browning. They sell somewhere between three thousand and four thousand dollars per gun. I've just never felt that I could afford such a gun.

I believe Ed Jones was the first man that I ever hunted with who had one of those guns. Ed had a twenty-gauge, over-and-under Browning that was a beautiful gun.

Ed told me at the evening meal how much quail hunting experience he had, how many quail he had killed, and it all boiled down to the fact that Ed Jones was an excellent shot. He wasn't bragging. That wasn't his intent, and I didn't take it that way. He was just telling a lot of his experiences, and he was telling me that he was a good shot. I accepted that as a fact; he was and is a good shot.

We took off grouse hunting the next morning. At the first grouse that we found, the dog, we had an English pointer, pointed. Ed Jones and I walked up to that dog.

I said, "Now, Ed, it's your shot. I can kill birds any time up here. You're just here for the day, so you take the shot."

The bird came up. Ed Jones raised that expensive gun up and fired one time. He hit that grouse, but the grouse didn't fall. I know he hit it because when he shot, the bird altered its flight pattern and went into a spiral, twenty yards in diameter, and flew up and up and up to about three hundred feet. Then, it peeled off to the left and sailed clear out of sight. We didn't even look for it; we had no idea where that bird went, but it got away.

We went on hunting. By lunch time, we had opportunity after opportunity to kill a grouse. The dog pointed time and time again, probably up to as many as fifteen times by lunch time. Every time that dog pointed a grouse, Ed Jones and I walked up behind that dog to shoot that grouse. Invariably, that grouse would come up. Several times, Ed shot twice at a grouse, and when he didn't hit it, I shot once or twice at it. Not one single grouse did we hit. I didn't see one single feather out of a grouse. We were evidently missing them completely.

We ate lunch and took about a thirty-minute rest and started hunting again. The dog would point. Ed Jones and I would go up behind that dog, a grouse would come up, and we would miss it anywhere from two to three to five times. We hunted all afternoon. Before we got back to the truck, I said, "Now, Ed, it's just two hundred yards to the truck. If you're going to kill a grouse, you'd sure better hit the next one if we find another one."

At that time we calculated that we had had twenty-five points; twenty-five times we had walked up behind that bird dog to kill a grouse, and twenty-five times the bird came up, and twenty-five times we missed it.

We were getting close to the truck, time to go home. I said, "Ed, time's up. You might have one more chance; you might not have any chances."

Sure enough, before we got back to the truck, the dog pointed again, making twenty-six times. I said, "Now, Ed, I'm not going to shoot. This is your bird."

We walked to the dog, and I just stood back and watched Ed. He flushed that bird. It came up and just flew straight away across the valley, with not one single, solitary twig or bush of any kind in the way. Ed shot that four-thousand-dollar gun twice and that bird went on.

We got back in the truck. Ed Jones said, "I know it happened. I was in on it. I saw it happen. But I still don't believe it. I will never believe that you and I hunted that long, had twenty-six grouse pointed, and shot probably seventy-five times, and we didn't kill one single, solitary bird."

After you miss a certain number of birds, it affects your central nervous system. It affects your confidence. It's the same psychological effect as the one afflicting a baseball player in a hitter's lump, who simply can't hit a thing.

Ed Jones has come back and hunted with me several times over the years. We've killed a lot of birds. But that one day, the opening day of our partnership, was twenty-six to nothing.

Ruth Jones's Grouse

Carl Jones and his wife, Ruth Hughes Jones, live in an area some ten miles from our Harrell Hill community. Still, I have known them and their family for many years. Miss Ruth has been a favorite of mine since she walked into a classroom some forty years ago, sporting an impish grin and a mannerism that caused me to make a mental note to the effect that, "You'd better keep your eye on this one, keep her under control, or she'll be dancing a jig right out here on the classroom floor."

Down through the years I've averaged seeing this couple five or six times every year. Ninety-five percent of the time, Ruth still has that impish grin, but I have seen her when her heart was breaking as she struggled to give therapy to a grown son that had been injured in an automobile accident. But this story is about something else.

In 1991, I was having lunch one day out at Dolly and Kyle Bailey's cafe in Loafer's Glory. I had company at my table, two gentlemen of about my age. We get together once a month or so and have lunch and tell tales and lies and what have you. While we were having lunch, Ruth Hughes Jones came in with a sister of hers and one or two other people, and they took a table nearby.

When Ruth looked back over the cafe and saw me, she got up from her table and came back to mine and pulled up a chair and said, "Mr. Harrell, I killed a grouse. I killed a grouse! I want you to know that I killed a grouse."

"Well, Ruth, that's wonderful. Just simmer down and tell me all about it."

Here's the story I got:

Ruth had walked into a room of her house some time earlier, and her husband and one of their grown sons were busy getting on their hunting equipment, getting their guns, getting their shells and so forth.

Ruth said, "What do you fellows think you are going to do?"
"We are going grouse hunting."

"Do you think you are going to leave me here at the house? I'm going with you."

Her son said, "Mom, that'll be fine. We'll be real happy for you to go along, but we don't have any gun for you. We just have two shotguns, and Dad has one and I have the other one."

"That's all right. I'll take my twenty-two rifle."

So they take off; get up on the side of a mountain. The dog points, and all three of them move up to where the dog is. Ruth is kind of hanging off to one side with her little twenty-two rifle. The bird comes up and flies out across the valley. It's just about to reach the top of the hill when these big twelve-gauge shotguns go **KAROOM, KAROOM**. The bird goes on, with no sign of its being touched. Ruth puts this twenty-two rifle up to her shoulder and pulls the trigger. It goes SPAT. And the blessed bird falls. She had hit that bird out at about sixty yards with that twenty-two rifle.

Well, they got the bird, danced a jig around it, and whooped and hollered and carried on. Ruth finally took the bird in and took it to someone and had it mounted and has it in her home today as proof of the bird that she killed with that twenty-two rifle.

It's my understanding that when that date rolls around on the calendar each year the Jones family declares it to be a national holiday. They all quit their work and come in home on that particular day. After lunch, they hit the hills to go grouse hunting again. They haven't told me whether they take shotguns or whether they take twenty-twos.

A Young Man's First Grouse Hunt

A student studying law at Mercer University in Macon, Georgia, called me and talked me into taking him on his first grouse hunt. He came to my place sometime after two or three telephone conversations, and I took him grouse hunting, with my dog of course.

His name was Chuck Watson, and he was a pleasant young man.

I took him to an area that I knew had some birds in it. We hunted some half a day, probably, and the young man killed three grouse. That's real unusual for anyone that's never shot grouse to kill a limit of birds. But this young man had hunted quail and he knew how to handle a gun and he knew about pointing dogs. When the opportunity presented itself that afternoon, he was lucky enough to kill the limit of grouse.

Of course he was real happy and he thanked me profusely. When he went back to his university in Macon, Georgia, he wrote a letter to Mr. George Bird Evans, the author of a book entitled An *Affair With Grouse.* That young man ordered a copy of Mr. Evans's book, to be sent to me. When I received the book, the letter was enclosed. I will quote from the letter here. It will do a better job of saying what I want to say than I could do myself.

"While I have hunted quail, and my father and grandfather have hunted quail, I sought to experience a bit of the tradition about which you write so beautifully. Under Mr. Harrell's tutelage I was fortunate enough to take my limit in the snowy peaks around Roan Mountain. While no adept, I am a convert."

———————•——•——

CHAPTER TWO

Bird Dogs

How to Train a Bird Dog

The bird dogs that I have grouse hunted with have been dogs that I have trained myself. I start them as pups, when they are old enough to get around on the lawn, which means when they are about six or seven weeks old. I have always in my training put strong emphasis on teaching the dog to retrieve, and not only on teaching him to retrieve, but teaching him to love to retrieve.

I start this retrieving teaching by rolling or bouncing a ball in front of the puppy and away from me. If I don't bounce the ball over five or ten feet, the pup will see it and, with his playful disposition, will want to go get it in his mouth. With a little encouragement, you can get the pup to bring the ball back to you. I like to repeat this three or four times, but no more than that. It is extremely important to stop the retrieving lesson before the pup gets tired. Then, when you retrieve again, he looks at it as something of fun and play.

As the pup gets older, I change from throwing the retrieving ball out in the lawn to throwing a retrieving dummy (made of grouse feathers stuffed in a man's sock) out into weeds or tall grass where the pup can't see it. He has to change from looking with his eyes to smelling with his nose to locate the ball. I keep this up for a period of about six or seven months, doing it probably twice a day.

Again, I emphasize to not do the retrieving more than three or four times at one lesson. If you go beyond the time that the dog gets tired of retrieving, then you've lost his interest, and he wants to do something else. I want to emphasize to the dog that this is fun; we are having fun and you are not working. You are having fun bringing this ball back to your master.

I watch the pup real carefully to read when he is showing signs of lack of interest or of being tired, and I may not take up the lesson again for another day.

You can teach a dog to despise retrieving by forcing him to do too much at a time. I don't like to teach a dog anything by force. I prefer teaching him by interest, excitement, and play, really, by a desire to please his master. Over the years I have been able to teach these pups several things and make fine bird dogs out of them. Over the years these same pups have taught me many things.

In teaching the pup to retrieve, I use the term "fetch it." It's not good English, perhaps, but the dog seems to understand it, and it has a ring about it that the dog can pick up real quick. When I say "fetch it" to my dogs when they are about six months old, they know to bring something to me.

After I have gone through the process of teaching the young pup to retrieve with the ball on the lawn, then switching to some type of dummy to throw out in the weeds to let the dog learn to

Five-month-old Brittany pups, pointing grasshoppers.

hunt with his nose—after I've gone through those processes until I'm sure the dog understands what we're doing and what I mean by the term "fetch it"—I like to take the pup out in the field and shoot for him a dove or a grouse or a quail or some game bird. It is amazing how quickly and with how much interest that pup will pick up a game bird for the first time and bring it to me. Nine times out of ten, he will come to within ten steps of me and stop. He is enjoying the feel of those feathers in his mouth so much and the excitement of having something with a game odor to it that he just doesn't want to give up the bird.

Here is a point of extreme importance: I *never* take that bird away from that young dog. I talk to him and give him a little encouragement, then I'll walk on. Out of the corner of my eye, I'll watch that dog. He'll carry that bird for a while. Sometimes I've had a dog carry that bird for as long as fifteen minutes before he gets tired of carrying it and lays it down in front of me because he doesn't know what else to do with it.

Had I taken that bird away from that dog when he came in ten feet of me the first time, he would have turned away from me in future retrievings and would have been tempted to run away from me with the bird in his mouth. I want to point out to any man who is training a young pup, let the pup carry the first bird that he retrieves just as long as he wants to carry it.

He may want to carry the second, third, or fourth bird he retrieves. Let him carry the birds just as long as he wants to carry them. After a while, he will come to you and lay that bird down fairly close to you. When the dog does that, I stop and rub him on the head. I pet him and tell him what a fine dog he is and what a fine job he has done. Pretty soon, he will learn that when he picks up a bird in retrieving, he goes to his master to be encouraged and to be bragged on and to be petted.

Using that method, I have had many fine retrievers that get as big a kick out of bringing a bird to me as I do seeing them pick up the bird and make a fine retrieve.

I have been out with a few hunters whose dogs have been taught by force to retrieve. I don't need to go into complete detail on that. But they use the force method, by putting a collar on a dog and putting a rope on him and throwing out an object and forcing him, by pulling on the rope, to bring the bird back. That will work, but a dog that has been taught to retrieve by the force method does not retrieve with the same fun and enthusiasm and pleasure as my dogs retrieve as a result of the method of training I use with them.

When I hunt by myself (and most of my hunting is done alone, just the dog and me), the dog rides on the truck seat beside me. I put a towel or something on the seat to protect it from muddy or dirty feet. With that in place, the dog sits up beside me, tense and alert to everything along the side of the road. On those occasions that he sees a chicken or another dog beside the road, he becomes so animated that I put my hand on his head to calm him down. That is the picture as we drive from my house to the hunting area.

Many days in the 1960s, the dog and I would hunt until we killed the limit of three birds, then we'd go back to the truck. I would put my game bag with the three birds in it in the back of the truck, put my gun back behind the seat on a place specially prepared for it, then the dog and I would get in for the ride home.

On that ride home, the dog would sit up for about two or three minutes, looking straight ahead. Then, as he got sleepy and started resting from a hard day's hunt, he would lay down and put his head over on my right leg and go sound asleep. He would sleep from that time until we got into the driveway at the house.

This has happened to me more times than most fellows will ever kill a limit of grouse. The picture of that fine dog who has done

A.D. Harrell and the English setter Sam; Wisconsin, 1980. The pole structure in the background is an illegal bear trap rigged by poachers.

such a good day's work, laying on that truck seat, with his head on my leg, sound asleep, just as happy as he can be along with me being happy, is a picture that I wish I could put in color some way, that I wish I could put on canvas.

That is so different from an episode that I read about recently, where a dog owner picked his dog up, after the dog did something that the owner disapproved of, and threw that dog. It happened that the dog went over a rock cliff and was ruined. There was so much damage the dog never had any faith in his master any more.

This is a situation that is not going to happen with me and my dogs. We build up a buddy-buddy relationship through kindness and through careful training that no harsh training can ever achieve. We build up a relationship that is too valuable ever to disturb by being cruel or being anything resembling cruel.

Lemon Dog

One of the most interesting dogs I have trained was a pointer pup that was solid white, except for his ears, which were a solid lemon color. For that reason, we named him "Lemon." Lemon Dog had an unusually interesting life. He was eager to learn. He was intelligent. He was a big dog, eighty pounds, probably, with a huge mouth, and teaching him to retrieve was a pleasure because he particularly enjoyed the retrieving.

When he was beginning his first hunting season, our two sons, Doug and Larry, and a friend of Larry's named Larry Boone, and I took Lemon on his first grouse hunting trip. We drove a truck out in the National Forest land and camped out overnight.

We hunters slept in the truck bed, under a cover that we had stretched from one corner of the truck to the other, like a Conestoga wagon set up. We tied Lemon underneath the truck, on a ten-foot leash, where he would be out of the weather and have a warm, dry place to sleep, yet be free to circle around a little bit.

Any time in the night when we four men needed to use the rest room, we would just get up, step up to the edge of the truck bed, and pee off the end of the truck. About four o'clock in the morning, some kind of commotion woke me up. It was our son Larry, saying, "Doug, you peed all over Lemon."

The next time I heard of that phrase was when our Larry and Larry Boone were in an English class together at Mitchell High School. The teacher was a fine English teacher named Miss McBee.

The class got kind of dull, evidently, and Larry Harrell and Larry Boone were sitting in rows next to each other, close enough to exchange whatever boys like to talk about during English class. Larry Harrell whispered to Larry Boone, "Doug, you peed all over Lemon."

Larry Boone burst out in a laugh, boisterous like, right there in the English class. The teacher didn't particularly like all that commotion going on, all that laughing, so she asked him what he was laughing about.

He said, "I'm laughing about what Larry told me."

She asked, "What did Larry tell you?"

He said, "Do you really want to know?"

"Yes. I want to know."

"What Larry Harrell told me was, 'Doug, you peed all over Lemon.'"

That broke up the English class.

The next episode in Lemon's life was interesting. The following summer, a State Highway Department crew was working on the road in front of our house. Come lunch time, they parked their vehicles at the community house, at the bottom of our church lawn area. They got their lunches out and were cooking some stuff so as to have a hot lunch.

Lemon Dog was running loose, so he cruised up there, I guess, to see what was going on. Maybe he smelled their lunch or something. While I was having lunch, I looked out the dining room picture window, where I could see the highway, and here comes Lemon with a full loaf of bread.

He came up the porch with it. I went out there, and he gave it to me. I looked it over and saw that the cover wasn't broken, so I knew what had happened. He had gone up to see those road crew workers and had cruised through their territory where they were sitting. He saw a loaf of bread laying there and he thought, "Well, I guess my master would like a loaf of bread," so he picks up the loaf and brings it home.

I got in the vehicle and took the bread back up there. I said, "Boys, what happened?"

"That so-and-so dog of yours came through here like a cyclone, picked up the only loaf of bread we had, and took off down the road. The louder we yelled, the faster he ran, so we gave up."

I gave them their loaf of bread. They thanked me for bringing it back, but they didn't have many kind remarks for Mr. Lemon.

As the summer went on, such things continued to happen. My aunt, who lived about a half a mile from us, was selling hatching eggs for people to raise broilers from. They would buy the eggs from Aunt May and put them in a hatchery and raise young chicks. To get these eggs, my Aunt May had about a hundred hens. She had them pretty well enclosed in a poultry-wire fence, but that fence didn't keep out Mr. Lemon.

About five or six times during that summer, up on the porch would come Mr. Lemon with a white Leghorn hen in his mouth, not injured at all. She would have her head up and be half scared to death, of course, but he hadn't hurt her. I'd get the hen and get in my vehicle and take it back up. I'd stick that hen back inside the pen. (I always tried to do it when Aunt May wasn't around.)

That happened time and time again. I don't think he ever killed one and I don't think Aunt May ever found out he was carrying them off and I was bringing them back, but we went through a summer like that.

Lemon was still running loose when school started that fall. At that time, we had a clothesline stretched behind the house, where the winter sun hit. When Geneva did the wash, she hung her freshly washed clothes on this clothesline to dry. Two or three evenings when I came in from school, she would say, "That Lemon

Dog drug one of your shirts off my clothesline and just ruined it—drug it right through the mud and messed it up something awful."

Geneva would go on to tell me how she would wash the clothes, get them nice and clean, take 'em out in the sun, hang 'em on the clothesline to dry. Within an hour, that Lemon Dog would have one piece of those clean clothes in his house, messed up completely. She would proceed to get her a switch and she'd switch that dog. The next week they'd go through the same thing.

I heard that story several times over a period of two months. Eventually, Mr. Lemon learned that it wasn't wise to bother anything on that clothesline. He learned that it was just bad business.

One day I came in and Geneva said, "I taught Mr. Lemon to let my clothesline alone, not to be pulling things off of it. I am fed up with that to the bone, and I've taught him one more lesson."

What Geneva had done was to turn off the controller on the electric fence, go to the barn and get a piece of electric fence wire, and hook it from the controller to her clothesline. She fixed it so the clothesline wire would be hot. Then, she took a wet white sheet and hung it on the clothesline, so that the bottom was about three feet from the ground. She checked on Lemon, who was lying in the sun, with his nose on his paws, watching her.

With everything fixed up, she turns on the controller and goes into the house where she can see the sheet and see Lemon.

He gets up and stretches. He looks to the right. He looks to the left. He looks towards the door. He takes about five steps towards that clothesline and he stops and he looks again to make sure there is nobody watching him. Then, he marches over to that white sheet. He stands on his hind feet and opens that big mouth wide enough to swallow a third of the sheet. He gets a corner of it and shuts his mouth.

He lets out a war whoop, jumps about two feet off the ground, goes flying back to his house, yelping with every breath, and crawls inside. He just barely sticks his nose out of his house and lays there for thirty minutes and whimpers.

"I don't believe he'll bother the clothesline any more," said Geneva.

He *didn't* bother the clothesline. Nor did he retrieve like he once did, either.

Sometime later, I took him hunting. He found a grouse and he pointed beautifully for about two seconds. Then, he started backing off, just walking backwards like he was scared. That clothesline episode with the hot sheet had shocked him so severely that he lost his confidence. He wasn't sure what was going to be hot and what wasn't. He points that grouse and he thinks, "Well, that sheet was hot, that grouse might be hot, so I'll just back off and leave it alone." So he came to me.

I reassured him and petted him and talked to him a little. We went on for about half an hour when the very same thing happened again. He pointed another grouse, then he backed off. Before I could get to him, he broke his point and came on back to me.

That behavior went on through three or four hunting trips. I saw then that the dog would never make a hunting dog. He had lost his confidence; he was afraid of everything. I had a fine, beautiful bird dog that was afraid to point.

I had an uncle who lived in Ohio at the time. He would come here for a week every now and then. For some reason, he got attached to Lemon. They got to be good friends. My uncle would play with Lemon, and Lemon would make a little over my uncle.

One day my uncle said, "I think a lot of that dog."

"Well that is good," I said, "because he is yours. I'm going to give him to you."

"You wouldn't give me that fine dog?"

I said yes and I told him what had happened. "He'll never make a hunter. He's had his confidence destroyed. But he's a fine, friendly dog. He'll make a fine watch dog, and he's a beautiful dog. I'm going to give him to you."

My uncle took him on to Ohio. Lemon lived to be fifteen and died of old age.

An Extra Bird

Mr. Charles Hill is the man who introduced me to grouse hunting in Wisconsin. Now, Charles Hill is a super gentleman. He is a graduate of North Carolina State University in the field of wildlife biology. He has been a partner in many of my grouse hunts over the years. In fact, we started hunting together in 1958, and we've hunted together at least a few times each season over the years from 1958 to the present time. Charles has finished his stint of duty with the North Carolina Wildlife Commission, and he is now in retirement. We still find time to grouse hunt.

In 1989 at Three Lakes, Wisconsin, one evening after our evening meal, Charles Hill came to our camp and visited awhile. He and his wife were staying in another cabin. When he came to our camp, he said, "A.D., there is a place I hunted a day or two ago, and I'd like to take you there in the morning, if you can break away from your party."

I told him I could do that, and we agreed to go the next morning at eight o'clock.

The next morning at about eight o'clock, Charles came by. We took my dog and his dog. We drove east out of Three Lakes, on

Forest Service Road 2183, toward Wisconsin State Highway 55. On the right side of Forest Service Road 2183, as we traveled east, Charles Hill had found an area of some two or three hundred acres that had been developed by the Wisconsin Wildlife Commission with the help of the National Grouse Society. They had done some special planting and some special work in some special areas to make the habitat more attractive to ruffed grouse.

Charles and I walked into the area, after we had parked our vehicle, for about three- or four-hundred yards, until we came to a fork in the road. Charles took his Brittany and went to the right, and I took my Brittany and went to the left. We had agreed that we would be back at that fork within one hour.

After we separated, my Brittany, Rusty, pointed. A grouse came up and I fired one time and the grouse fell. Rusty, who is a fine retriever, brought the bird to me. I held out my hand and he put the grouse in it. I put the grouse in my game bag and reached down and patted Rusty on the head and shoulders and told him what a fine dog he was and what a fine job he had done. I am convinced that dog knew exactly what I was saying, that I was bragging on his good job.

After I let him go, we went on for another fifteen or twenty minutes, then we repeated exactly the same thing. Rusty pointed again. A bird came up, and again I fired one time and that bird fell. Rusty went and got that bird and brought it back to me. I took the bird, put it in my game bag, and patted Rusty on the head and shoulders and bragged on him.

I noticed that while I was doing this the second time, Rusty seemed impatient. When I turned him loose, he went back into the bush where he had brought the bird from. In about three minutes, here he came with another bird.

I did not know what to think. I had not seen two birds flush, I had not seen two birds when I shot, and I am convinced that two birds did not flush. Anyway, I took the grouse and examined it real carefully. It was still warm, but it was not as warm as the first two that Rusty brought in, which meant that some other hunter had shot that grouse an hour or thirty minutes before we got there.

In going to get the bird I shot, Rusty had come across this other bird, and knew it was out there. Rusty gave me the bird I had shot and I took it and put it in my bag, then he went out and brought me this bird. I had shot twice and I had three grouse in my bag.

By then it was time for me to turn around and go back to the fork of the road to meet Charles Hill. I got there about the time Charles did, and he asked me how I had done.

I reached back into my game bag and handed him one grouse, then I reached in again and handed him the second grouse. Then, I reached back in my game bag and handed him the third grouse.

He said, "A.D., I didn't hear you shoot but two times."

"That's all I shot. I just shot two times."

"Well, you must have killed two birds with one shot."

"I don't know what happened, really. I shot the first time, the bird fell and the dog got it. Later on, I shot the second time, and the dog brought me one bird, then went back into the brush and brought me another bird. I really don't know what happened, but what I think happened was this: You recall as we came in here, we met some hunters who were going out. I don't recall their having a dog. I assume that they shot some grouse and couldn't find one of them. When we came in behind them an hour later, Rusty, being the fine retriever that he is, when he ran across this bird, he brought it to me."

———————•◆•———————

Rusty Dog

While I've started on Rusty and have him on my mind, let me do a little more bragging on that fine Brittany. When he was seven months old, I took him to Wisconsin for the first time. He was the third dog in the party. We had two highly trained dogs and we didn't hunt Rusty an awful lot, but we did hunt him enough to introduce him to the sport. That year there were a lot of birds, and Rusty got quite a bit of experience on that trip. We kept him up there two weeks and hunted him about an hour a day. We hunted the older dogs the rest of the time.

During those two weeks, he liked retrieving so well, till in two weeks Rusty kept going back into the woods where I had killed birds. Seven times within two weeks, he brought back birds that had flown out beyond sight after I had shot them. I didn't know I had hit them because I hadn't seen them fall, hadn't seen any feathers, hadn't seen a thing. But seven times in two weeks Rusty went out there in the brush and brought back a bird. Of course that moved him way up on the ladder of importance.

On another occasion I was hunting with Rusty in Mitchell County, North Carolina, in a section called Beans Creek. We were going up a log road or a drag trail (I use those terms interchangeably). Rusty went up in front of me about twenty-five yards and pointed, facing to the right. I went up behind Rusty and turned, ready to shoot the way he was pointing. About the time I got to him, a bird flushed on the other side of the road, on the left. I turned to the left and by the time my eyes picked up the bird it was fairly far out. I fired and it fell on top of a rock ledge or cliff. I looked at that situation and decided there was no way that I could get to that bird. I just couldn't crawl up that rock face in that heavy brush to get to it, and Rusty hadn't seen it fall. He had been looking the other way.

Rusty on point; Wisconsin, 1988. The grouse being pointed is in the spruce bushes in the lower right of the photograph.

But when I shot, Rusty broke point and came and stood beside me. I waved my hand in the direction of the rock ledge and said, "Fetch it, Rusty. Dead bird. Fetch it, Rusty."

Rusty went down the bank of the road, across a stream, and up the face of that rock. He was making loops to the right and to the left, going up about ten feet every time he made a loop. After about ten minutes of this, he reached the top of that ledge, picked up that bird, and brought it back to me.

Rusty is a good one.

Big John and Rusty Dog

Big John hunted with me so many times over a long period of time till just the involvement of natural events I assigned him one of my grouse dogs. I assigned him a dog named Tim, one of the very finest dogs I've had.

When John was here and just he and I were hunting, we would usually hunt with Tim, and I'd let John do the dog handling. When we'd go to Wisconsin, we'd take at least two dogs, and we'd have four to six men, usually, on those trips. I'd assign Tim to John, which meant John and one other man and Tim would be hunting in a party, and Doug and I with another dog, Rusty, would be hunting in a party.

On one such occasion, after we had hunted two or three days, John hunting with Tim and handling Tim, and myself and my other buddies with Rusty, Tim Dog developed an infection in one of his front feet. It got so severe, we had to rush him to a veterinarian in the area and keep him fastened up for about two days until the infection was under control. During that time, John didn't have the dog to hunt with.

During one of those afternoons, about three o'clock, I said to John, "You take our Rusty Dog, here, and take this area north of the road." We had hunted in this area several times, and I knew it to be a real good grouse area.

"You take Rusty and go in there and see know you get along. Maybe you can find something. Doug and I'll hunt on the other side of this road, without a dog. We'll meet you back here in two hours or so from now."

Doug and I took off in the opposite direction from John. We were within ear shot of him. I heard John shoot a time or two, and I was real anxious to know how he and Rusty got along. We came back to the meeting point some two hours after we had separated, and John and Rusty came on in.

Rusty and Tim Dog admiring A.D.'s grouse; Wisconsin, 1992.

I said, "John, how did you do? How did you and Rusty get along?"

"A.D., that dog can absolutely do no wrong. I have never seen a finer performance in my life than that dog put on. He pointed seven different birds. I killed five of them. He retrieved them, every single one, and brought 'em right back to me. His performance was just perfection. I am just real high on that dog. After I killed my five birds (the limit in Wisconsin), I unloaded my gun and came on back. As we came back out, that dog pointed two more birds I could have shot. He is a dandy, and we had a great two hours of hunting."

That is an example of helping your buddy have a good time and making everybody enjoy themselves that much more because of the effort that you put forth.

Tim Dog

Any grouse hunter that hunts with his own dogs knows if those dogs are good (and there is no use taking one out unless it's well trained and is obedient and knows what it's doing). They can be so good that a man is intensely proud of them. A hunter can't hunt many days without bragging to somebody about how good his dog is. Forgive me while I tell you another story about how proud I am of my dogs and how good one particular dog is.

In Wisconsin a few years ago, a friend of mine, Big John, was hunting with one of my dogs, a dog named Tim, a Brittany spaniel. John was hunting in the Nicolet National Forest, beside an area that had been torn up by a tornado the previous summer, leaving a whole mess of debris on the ground. It was impossible to walk through that downed timber and downed brush. John was walking along an old road that skirted the edge of the blown down timber, when Tim Dog pointed a grouse for him. John came up behind the dog, and the grouse came up and flew over this downed timber. John shot the bird; it fell about forty yards out in that brush and downed timber.

Tim Dog is a splendid retriever. He will go to those birds and get them, and bring them back to the man, put them in the man's hands and give them to him. But once out of, probably, every fifty birds he retrieves, he will not bring the bird back to the man. He will dig a hole in the ground, put that bird in the ground, and (this has always amazed me) cover it up. He doesn't cover it up with his feet. He takes his nose and pushes leaves and brush and debris on that bird and walks off about his business as if nothing happened. There is no way on earth you can find that bird; there is no way we've ever been able to get Tim to go back and dig up that bird for us. We have never found one that he has buried, unless we saw him bury it. And I've seen him bury two or three.

Tim went after that bird John shot. Being a small dog, Tim was able to get through the debris by crawling under the logs and brush. Big John could hear his bell tinkling and knew where he was. Big John could tell when his bell stopped tinkling that he had reached the bird. John could tell pretty well by the noise of the bell, the starting and stopping, what Tim was doing. He had picked that bird up and he was trying to come back to John through that brush.

John waited some fifteen minutes. Tim's bell went out of hearing. It ceased and Tim did not come, so John thought, "He has buried my bird and left."

In about five more minutes, Tim came back to John, but he didn't come out of the brush the way he went in. He came down

Tim brings one in; Wisconsin, 1988.

the road, far around the brush, that he and John had traveled
when they left the truck and went into the grouse hunting
country.

"Tim," said John, "where's my bird? Where's my bird!"

John says Tim didn't say a thing.

"You and I are going to go hunt that bird," John said to Tim. So
John crawled and struggled, Tim right along with him, and finally
got through the brush to where that bird fell. There he found
feathers on the ground, a considerable number of feathers. He

tracked the direction the dog had carried that bird a little ways by the feathers on the ground, but he couldn't find the bird. John marked the spot where the bird had fallen, then he started making a circle around and around it on his hands and knees, with the circle getting a little larger all the time, looking over every foot of ground for the place that the dog had buried that bird.

"Tim! You get down here now," said John, "and help me hunt that bird. I can't smell so I can't find that bird, and you've got to help me."

John said Tim didn't say a word, didn't even look interested. John hunted and he hunted and he hunted, but he couldn't find the bird. He finally said to Tim, "You buried the bird. That's bad, real bad. Don't know what to think about you."

With that, they left the brush, crawled back to the road, and walked the quarter of a mile to the truck. John walked around to the driver's side and started to open the door. There lay that grouse, right there beside of the truck.

When a dog picks up a bird as big as a grouse, the dog has to hold his head up because of the weight of the bird. With his head up and that bird in his mouth, Tim couldn't get through the brush, so he circled the brush getting out of there. He came out fairly close to the truck. At that point, Tim didn't know where John was, so he took the grouse to the truck and laid it down, then went to get John. That's how good my dog was.

If Tim could talk, he would have said to John, "Come on, dummy. The grouse is already out by the truck. Let's get out of this brush!"

Portrait of Rusty

In the county of Mitchell, North Carolina, there lives an artist by the name of Hannah Bennett. She lives in the Brummett's Creek area, about ten miles west of where my family lives. It has been my good fortune for the last fifty or sixty years to be friends with Hannah Bennett and her husband, Ed. Mr. Bennett passed away some ten years ago, but Hannah still lives in the old homestead, by herself.

I stop and see her every time I'm hunting in the area, and in the winter time my grandsons and I have taken her a load or two of wood. We cut firewood to the specifications of her wood stove and haul her a load or two of wood and stack it in a dry place for her to have during the winter, just an indication of how much we think of Hannah Bennett.

Hannah is a super artist, considering the fact that she hasn't had a lot of formal art training. For an untrained artist, she is about the best I have ever seen. You can give her a picture, say six by four, and say you would like to have a twenty-four by twenty portrait of it, and in a month she'll hand you an oil painting that will make your eyes bug out.

Now, I've been bragging on Rusty. In 1992 I went to Hannah Bennett and said, "Hannah, I know how good an artist you are, and you know how much I think of you. Here's something I want you to do. At my age, my grouse hunting years are coming to a close. I hope to hunt a few more years. Really, I hope to hunt ten more years, but I may or I may not. I want you to take this color picture of my dog, Rusty. And I want you to do me an oil portrait on canvas, twenty-four by twenty. I don't want you to spare any expense. I want you to do the very best possible job you can."

The snapshot that I gave her to paint from was a picture of Rusty coming back to me with a grouse in his mouth. It just so happened that the grouse was upside down, as Rusty came to me, with its tail fanned out in a beautiful fan, and the light effect on the grouse and the dog, Rusty, was real good.

Some month after I gave the picture to Hannah Bennett, she called me and said, "A.D., your picture is ready. You can come pick it up any time." I made a specified date and time that I would be there.

When that date came around, I went to get the portrait. She handed it to me, and I stepped back to take a look at it. To look at a portrait like that, you can't hold it in your hands, right up to your face, and look at it. You've got to set it down on a table or set it against a wall or something, and back up about ten feet to really appreciate it.

I set that portrait on her piano and I stepped back to the other side of the room.

Hannah Bennett had done an excellent job.

I don't know of anything of this nature in my possession that I value as much as I value this portrait. Today, July 1994, that portrait of Rusty retrieving the grouse is hanging in our living room, in a place of honor. It is my desire that when I stop grouse hunting and pass on some of the things that we have put together and have saved, things to pass on to our fine children and grandchildren, that this portrait go to a son or a grandson. I think knowing how much they have enjoyed hunting with me, when I realize how much those grandsons have enjoyed hunting with Daddy Dee (they call me "Daddy Dee," all the grandchildren do), they will appreciate the portrait that Hannah Bennett painted of Rusty just as much as I have.

I suppose that it is a trait of the human character that as men get older they become a little more soft hearted, more sentimental, a little more easily touched. When Hannah Bennett gave me the portrait, I was seventy-six years old. I paid her for the portrait and gave her a handsome tip, and walked out the door. As foolish as it

Portrait of Rusty; photograph used by Hannah Bennett to paint Rusty's picture.

seems, here's a man of seventy-six years old, carrying a painting of his bird dog. I was fighting back tears from her door to my car.

Since we have two sons, I needed one more portrait of a bird dog. I went to Hannah Bennett again and had her paint a portrait of a Brittany bird dog named Dottie, so I can give that one to one son and the painting of Rusty to the other son. The "Dottie" portrait now hangs in our son Doug's living room.

CHAPTER THREE

Mostly Tales
from the Grouse Woods

———◆———

Geneva Road

In our Wisconsin grouse hunt in 1987, we took Geneva and Barbara with us. Barbara is Doug's wife, Geneva's and my daughter-in-law, and just happens to be one of the finest daughters-in-law anyone could have. We think the world of her and have enjoyed having her in the family. There are many other good things I could say about her; she is just simply a jewel.

Each of the two ladies owns a twenty-gauge, semi-automatic shotgun, and they can handle them fairly well. As to Geneva's ability to handle her gun, I recall this incident. Two or more years before this hunt we had a dove shoot on our farm. We had some five or six men lined up on the ridgeline here, shooting at doves. It just happened during that particular set up that Geneva was on the north end of that line, and doves were flying up and down that ridgeline from north to south and south to north. On one occasion, a dove came across from the south end and flew to the north, which meant it was flying over that line of men. That dove flew over me; I shot a time or two, and it went on. That dove flew over Doug; he shot, and it went on. It flew over Lester Miller; he shot at it, and it went on. It flew over Norris Masters, who was the last man on the line before Geneva, and he shot at it a time or two and that dove went on. Geneva put up that twenty-gauge shotgun and pulled the trigger. That dove fell.

71

I remember to this day what Norris said. He called to me, "Did you see that!" Well I had. I had seen that. So, Geneva was a pretty good shot with that gun and has been quite an outdoorsman.

On the Wisconsin trip, we were out hunting one afternoon, just Geneva and I and a dog. The vehicle had dropped us off and the rest of the party had gone on to hunt in other areas and were going to come back and pick us up. Geneva and I started off down a trail in the forest, in Nicolet National Forest, and the dog pointed. The dog was in front of us about fifteen or twenty yards; he flipped his head to the left and pointed. We walked on up to him. Geneva stopped on the left side of the dog, and I placed myself on the other side. We had the dog between us and hopefully some grouse out in front of us.

When we were both ready, I flipped a little rock or something out in front of the dog. My memory says three grouse came up, flying away from us. The grouse closest to me offered me a good shot. I raised my gun, got on that bird and pulled the trigger. The bird fell. I didn't take my gun down; I just swung it around to the left, toward Geneva's shooting area, thinking I might get another shot on that side, because I knew at least two more birds had come up. As I came around to the left, Geneva shot, and I just dropped my gun barrel because the bird she shot was coming down. So, she shot one time, and I shot one time, and we had two birds.

When our vehicle came up, we got out our maps of that area and we named the road "Geneva Road." That name is on all of our Wisconsin maps, and each time we go, we stop there and recall, in memory at least, the two birds that Geneva and I got there.

We named another road in Wisconsin the "Barbara and Geneva Road." One day, Doug and I left Geneva and Barbara at the cabin. I don't remember now why, but they were agreeable to being left.

Barbara and Doug Harrell; Wisconsin, 1994. Photo by Geneva Harrell.

Maybe they wanted to do some hiking around, looking for Indian relics, or something of that nature. When we came back, they said, "We have things to tell you."

They had walked up the highway a piece and had gone off onto a hunting trail and had flushed seven birds. They killed one or two of those birds. They were having a ball, of course.

Good Samaritans

During the time that Geneva and our daughter-in-law Barbara went with us on this Wisconsin trip in 1987, we were involved in an incident having to do with an automobile accident. On our trips to Wisconsin, we rent a cabin from Carl and Jean Kubley at Joy Villa in Glidden, Wisconsin. One morning about two-thirty, somebody came to the door of that cabin and knocked on the door.

It happened that Geneva was on her feet, going to or from the bathroom. She heard the knock and went to the door and turned on the porch light. Standing outside that door were two young men in real bedraggled looking clothing, wet and unkempt and so forth. Geneva automatically showed some fear and concern about what was going on here.

The fellow that was doing the talking said, "Lady, please don't be afraid of us. We've had a real serious accident down the road here. We left three men out there, and one of them may be dead by this time. This was the first house that we came to. We walked for some distance, and this was the first house we came to. Please help us if you can."

By that time, Doug and I were both awake and standing behind Geneva, listening to what was going on. The two men told this story. Somewhere down the road nearby, their car had left the road and had turned over in the swamp. Two people were able to walk, and those two had come to our house. The other three were injured so badly that they were sitting beside the road, on the shoulder near where the car had wrecked. Of course we told them immediately that we would help them.

Doug and I dressed and with those two men went to the point of the accident. There we found three men who looked like they were in critical condition. All three were lying on the ground, not able to walk. Doug was driving his Suburban. That Suburban has three seats in it. We folded up the back seat and picked up the three men who were injured and put them in the back of that vehicle and closed the door. We asked the other two men if they knew where a hospital was. They didn't know.

The closest town of any size to us was Park Falls, some thirty-five miles south of where we were. We assumed there would be some type of hospital facility in Park Falls. Doug turned the vehicle around, and we headed down Highway 13 toward Park Falls in the middle of the night.

On Doug's Suburban is a two-way radio that we use for various things, to check on the weather and road conditions and this 'n that. Doug got on the two-way radio and put out this message, "A blue and gray Suburban with North Carolina license plates on it has on board three men who are critically injured from an accident. We are looking for a hospital. We don't know where a hospital is, but we are trying to find one. We are looking for help. Any sheriff's department, or highway patrol, or police department that hears this, please come in."

Immediately, we got this response, "This is the Park Falls Police Department, North Carolina Suburban with the injured men. We have your message. We'll assist in any way we can. Over."

Doug got back on and said, "We're on Highway 13. We're traveling south toward Park Falls. We have all lights flashing; we have all hazard lights on. We are traveling at an excessive rate of speed. Right now, our speedometer is reading eighty-five or eighty-six miles per hour. We need somebody to get us to a hospital ."

The police department at Park Falls came back on and said, "North Carolina Suburban, we have your message. We will put a police cruiser at the city limits of Park Falls. When you come into view, that police cruiser will pull out in front of you and will lead you to a hospital. We'll also have a second police cruiser there to pull in behind you and give you protection from the back."

Doug said we would be there in something like five or ten minutes. We were something like thirteen miles away, still doing eighty-five miles an hour.

The police department came back on and said that when we got to the Park Falls city limit to cut that speed down to something that was safe. When we got in view of Park Falls, there sat the two cruisers, as they had promised. One pulled out and led us to the eastern part of town, straight to the hospital. The second cruiser pulled in behind us.

We moved into the hospital safely and unloaded our three injured people at the emergency room. We signed some papers that told them our names, our addresses in North Carolina, and our telephone numbers and so forth. The police department signed a paper saying our actions were in compliance with Wisconsin's Good Neighbor Law. The Wisconsin Good Neighbor Law says in effect that if, in trying to assist an accident victim, that accident victim is further injured by the effort to assist him, there is no legal responsibility on the part of the person providing the assistance.

They took the injured people on into the emergency room. At that point, we lost sight of them. Doug and I got back in our vehicle and we drove back to Glidden, Wisconsin. We got back in time for breakfast with the rest of our group.

To this day, we've never heard from any of those five men. We don't know whether they lived or died, or how they got along.

Observing Birthdays on the Wisconsin Trip

An interesting sidelight to those Wisconsin hunts is the fact that my birthday is October the ninth. From 1972 until today, I have always had my birthday somewhere between here and Canada, in northern Wisconsin. I have made a game out of the situation.

When my birthday comes, wherever we happen to be eating that night, I make it a point to tell the waitress that I am having a birthday and that I am so old and that as of now I may be the oldest grouse hunter in the woods. Sometimes when I tell the waitress this, the cafe or restaurant gives me a free meal and the staff comes out and sings "Happy Birthday."

A few restaurants have gone along with that. They have given me a free meal, they have come out and sung "Happy Birthday," and they have even fixed cake and brought it out. Sometimes the cake is just a donut with some icing put on it and a match stuck in for a candle, but the staff gathers round and sings "Happy Birthday." In every single case when the cafe or restaurant has gotten into the spirit with us and agreed to give me a birthday dinner free and has sung to us and has provided something for a cake, be it a biscuit or a donut or what not, I have tipped that waitress a twenty-dollar bill. That has only happened three or four times in the twenty some years we have been going to Wisconsin.

I haven't been able to resist the desire to tell the waitress when she says that we can't do that–we just don't get involved in that kind of stuff–"Well, that's fine. I will be glad, of course, to pay for my meal, but I just want to tell you that you just missed a twenty-dollar tip."

Of course Geneva knows of my efforts to talk the cafe or restaurant or the waitress into giving me a free dinner and of my giving the waitress a twenty-dollar tip. She doesn't much approve of the idea at any time, so one year she baked a real big, fine birthday cake on about October the sixth, and packed it in a box so it wouldn't get torn up. She said, "When your birthday comes, you fellows get this cake out and you sing 'Happy Birthday' and you do whatever you want to do. But here's your birthday cake, so don't be trying to bribe those waitresses into giving you a free dinner and a free birthday cake."

We packed that box in the truck. We hauled it to Wisconsin. We hunted for two weeks, and then we started back home. We got to Indianapolis, Indiana, and I said, "Boys, we've got a birthday cake in that box that we were supposed to eat back on October the ninth. Here it is the nineteenth."

We hauled out that birthday cake in some cafe in Indianapolis, Indiana. We put candles on it and acted the fool and sang and cut up. We ate about one-fourth of the cake. We asked the staff to join us to eat the rest of the cake and they did. We had some big birthday celebration out of Geneva's cake, although we almost got back home with it before we thought about it.

Lost John Road

Talking about naming the roads in Wisconsin (there's the one named Geneva Road and the one named Barbara and Geneva Road), later on, two or three years later on, we named another road. We named that road the "Lost John Road," after my hunting partner, Big John.

I'll identify Big John. John had seen some service in World War II, when he was a young man, just out of high school. He came back and went to North Carolina State University and studied wildlife biology. He came out of that place with a degree in wildlife biology and took a job with the North Carolina Wildlife Commission. I got acquainted with John in 1956 or 1957.

John has been a prized and much appreciated grouse hunting partner down through the years. John has a great sense of humor. He has a big laugh for everybody, and he apparently has a good time wherever and whenever he goes out. He is retired now from the Wildlife Commission, but he still goes with us on that Wisconsin hunting trip. I make that statement to point out that here is a man who started hunting with me when he took his first job. He told me later on that his first assignment was to come to Mitchell County and see what A.D. Harrell wanted with some kind of wildlife problem. John hunted with me from the time he took his first job, through all of his working years, until his retirement.

Well, this time, John and I were hunting in Wisconsin by ourselves. At one o'clock in the afternoon, we were two miles from our hunting vehicle and had one dog. The dog went off down into some real swampy country, and John indicated that he didn't want to go down in there. I said, "I believe I'll go because that dog is mighty interested down there."

I went with the dog and left John sitting on the trail. I said, "Now John, I'll be back in a few minutes. Wait for me."

I went on down to where the dog was, found some birds, shot a time or two, then moved on down in there far enough till when I came back out on the trail, I didn't come back out where I went in. I came back out about a hundred yards closer to our truck than where I went in from. I assumed, since I had been gone so long and since we had been going back to the truck anyhow when I peeled off to go into the swamp, that John would continue on down the trail toward the truck and that we would get together at the truck and go on hunting from there.

I sat down beside the truck to wait for John. After a while, I took a piece of paper and wrote a note on it: "John, I'm hunting in an area north of the truck. I'll be back here in forty minutes. When you get back to the truck, wait for me."

I went off and hunted for forty minutes. When I came back, my note hadn't been touched, and John still wasn't there. At that point, I decided that John had probably come out on the gravel road that we had driven on, and that I would drive two miles down that gravel road in one direction, then come back and drive two miles down that road in the other direction and see if I could find him. I tore up the original note and wrote another one saying that I was going to ride the roads and that I would be gone thirty minutes, and saying to wait here for me.

I drove that truck west out that road for two miles. I came back to the starting point. The note was still there, so I drove out two miles in the other direction then came back. The note was still there. By then, it was getting to be three o'clock. I hadn't heard a shot. I hadn't heard a sound. I was getting to be real concerned about John.

At that point, I wrote another note and stuck it up on a stick, right in front of the truck. That note said, "I'm going to walk in the trail to where I left you. It will take me an hour to walk in there and back. You wait right here beside this truck for me."

I left the truck and I walked into the forest, to the log where I had left John sitting about one-thirty. He wasn't there. I wouldn't have been so concerned if I had been hearing some shots. I would have thought he was just hunting, having fun, killing some birds, and would be back after awhile. But I hadn't heard a shot from one o'clock to three. When I got to that log and John wasn't there, I got real concerned.

I went back to the truck. By then, it was four-thirty. This was late October, and at four-thirty it was not long until dark. I put another note on the stick and stuck it into the ground. That note said, "I have gone to town to get help to hunt you. Wait here."

On my way into town I met a truck coming from the direction that John and I had driven in. I stopped that truck and told the driver what the situation was, that I had a man lost. The fellow that I was talking to had a cabin back in there somewhere that he was going to. He said that he would watch for John and that if he found him, he would take care of him. I went on to town, to the place where we were staying, and called the sheriff's department to report a man lost, the number of the Forest Service road that he was on, and approximately where I had left him.

Then, I got in my truck and drove back to the point where I had left the notes. It was dark by then. When I got there, the note I had written was gone and another note was on the stick. The note said, "I have found John. I am taking him to the town of Glidden, to Mollie's Bar, and buying him a drink. John is all right. You can pick him up at Mollie's Bar."

I turned around and went back to town. I didn't know where Mollie's Bar was, but I pulled into a little store where we had bought some groceries. I opened the door and walked in, walked straight up to the counter. I hadn't had a chance to ask any question of any kind, when the clerk pointed her finger and said, "He's right across the street at that cafe."

Larry Harrell, Big John, Doug Harrell, and A.D. Harrell;
Wisconsin, 1982.

I went across the street, and there sat John, at that cafe. And I have never seen a good man angrier in my life. He was redder than fire. He wouldn't even speak. He was just downright furious with me for having the sheriff's department out hunting for him.

We ordered dinner and sat there and ate. He had to ride with me. If he had had any other way to have gotten back home, I don't think he would have ridden with me, he was so angry. But we ate dinner. Didn't say a word. Walked out and got back in our vehicle and started back to camp.

I said, "Now John, let me tell you something. I know you're a good woodsman. I know that you know your way around. I know that the chances are probably ninety-nine to one that you were all right, but I didn't know for sure. I hadn't heard you shoot. I hadn't heard tell of you for three hours. Although I suspected the chances were ninety-nine to one that you were all right, I want to tell you right now that where the safety of a buddy of mine is concerned, I will not take that one chance. That one chance is just too much to take, and I will not take one chance on your safety or on the safety of anyone else in this party, and I want you to understand that."

John kind of simmered down and saw that I was right in the first place, that I should have been hunting for him.

We named that road "Lost John Road." Every time we mention it, he still gets red in the face. He'll say a curse word and then say, "I wasn't lost. I have never been lost. I never intend to get lost. The only one who was lost was you lost from *me*."

Pineapple Upside Down Cake

In hunting over the years, Big John and I have had many pleasant incidents, many humorous incidents, many incidents that we recall with a great deal of laughter and amusement and appreciation. Some incidents we recall almost shamefacedly, one of which comes to mind at the present time.

When our grouse hunts started early in the morning, we would usually come back home about twelve-thirty to one o'clock. On those days, my fine wife, Geneva, would have lunch for us, a fine lunch with hot coffee, dessert, what have you.

Good cooks come in all classes and denominations and sizes and political persuasions and so forth. Excellent cooks are a little fewer. But when you get up to the super good cooks, there are very, very few. It has been my good fortune to have as a wife one of those super good cooks. Believe it or not, just across the road within two hundred yards of our house live my brother and his wife, Betty Jo, and Betty Jo is another super good cook. I have enjoyed the cooking expertise of both of these fine ladies.

One morning when we were ready to go grouse hunting, Geneva said, "Now you two boys come here into the kitchen. I want to show you something. I'm going shopping today, and I'm not going to be here to fix you any lunch when you come back in. But here in the refrigerator is," and she opened up the refrigerator, "a pineapple upside down cake that I made for you fellows for your dessert at lunch time. And here are various things on the stove, in the cabinets, and on the shelves around here that you can fix your own lunch with."

She thought that two men of reasonable ability ought to be able to fix their own lunch.

About twelve-fifteen we came back in, John and I did. Of course, Geneva was gone shopping. We looked in the kitchen and there were the things she had pointed out that we could fix our lunch with. We looked in the refrigerator and there was that fine pineapple upside down cake. Without a doubt, she bakes the best pineapple upside down cake I have ever tasted, and I have eaten desserts from Mexico to Canada. She is tops with the pineapple upside down cake.

We set that cake out on the table and looked at the things she had set out to cook lunch with. I decided that I didn't see anything that I wanted for lunch. I go to the telephone, and I pick up the telephone, and I dial Bruce and Betty Jo's number. Betty Jo answered the telephone.

I said, "Betty Jo, Big John and I have just come in, and we haven't had lunch. Would there be any possibility of us coming up there and you fixing lunch for us?"

Betty Jo said, "Well ..., well ..., I don't know. Well ... let me think about it a minute. Well ... let's see. ... Come on. I'll fix your lunch for you."

For some reason, John had brought with him that morning some sassafras roots to make sassafras tea with. John carried the sassafras roots and I carried the pineapple upside down cake to the vehicle, and we traveled up to Betty Jo's to impose on her to fix lunch for us.

She fixed a real good lunch. We ate and gossiped and laughed and acted the fool for thirty minutes. After lunch we cut that pineapple upside down cake, and John and I each had a big slice of it. We made about four glasses of sassafras tea. Bruce and Betty Jo had a glass of sassafras tea. John had a glass of sassafras tea, and I had a glass of sassafras tea.

But only John and I had pineapple upside down cake. For some unearthly reason (and I never know to this day why) we didn't offer Bruce and Betty Jo any pineapple upside down cake.

When things simmered down, we were ready to leave. We got up from the table, picked up our pineapple upside down cake, and down the road we came with that cake, what was left of it.

We walked into the living room. The telephone rang. It was Betty Jo. She said, "A.D., if I come down there with my cup of sassafras tea, would you give me a piece of that pineapple upside down cake?"

Out of there we went, carrying that pineapple upside down cake. Back up to Bruce and Betty Jo's we went. After Betty Jo called us on the carpet, we did give them some pineapple upside down cake.

Whose Bird?

In my sixty-five years of grouse hunting, my philosophy has been: See that your company or your partner has a good time. Do everything possible to see that he has a good day. Put him in the position of advantage to shoot. If the dog points and the situation is such that only one man can move up, put that partner in front and let him move up.

If the situation is such that both men can move up, we put a bracket on the dog (by "bracket" I mean one man moves up to the right side of the dog and the partner moves up to the left side of the dog, each man being some ten to fifteen feet away from the dog) and move up evenly or pretty well abreast of the dog. When

Big John and A.D. arguing about who shot the grouse; Mitchell County, North Carolina, 1966. Photo by Joel Arrington, North Carolina Division of Travel and Tourism.

the bird comes up, if the bird flies to the right, the man on the right end of the bracket shoots, and if the bird flies to the left, the man on the left shoots. If the bird flies straight away, frequently both men will shoot. If the bird falls, I try to disclaim any credit whatsoever for hitting that bird.

Frequently, I've had my partner ask, "Did you shoot?"

I would say, "No. I didn't shoot," when in reality I had shot. We had shot so much at the same time that my partner couldn't tell if I had shot or not. I wanted him to think that it was his bird—and it probably was.

I have found that over the years that practice cements a friendly relationship. Once the man realizes your intent is to help him have a good time, the whole day brightens up for everyone.

On one occasion when the dog pointed, Big John and I moved up to put a bracket on that dog; that is, one man moved up on the dog's left and one man moved up on the dog's right. On this particular occasion, I moved up on the left.

I got as far as I wanted to go, and I glanced back over my right shoulder to see where John was. He was having difficulty getting through some brush and briers and so forth to get up to the right side of the dog. John moved around to the right some distance and moved up in line with the dog, but some thirty yards away from the dog. All the time, I was standing guard while John was moving up. If the bird flushed before John got in position, I was ready to shoot it.

Eventually, John got in position, and we flushed the bird. It flew pretty well straightaway. I shot, which was shooting in behind the bird. John was shooting on the right side of the bird, on a diagonal. The bird fell. We each knew that the other man shot.

I said, "John, that's your bird. I couldn't have hit it because of the angle, the trajectory, and the brush and everything in my way. I couldn't possibly have hit that bird."

"Well, the way it was going, the way I had to shoot, I couldn't possibly have hit it, either."

We looked around. We said maybe there's a third man here; maybe somebody else hit that bird. But, we didn't find anybody else. By that time, the dog had brought the bird to me. I put it in my game bag.

We came on home that evening. I tried to give John the bird, but he wouldn't take it. He declared it wasn't his, he hadn't hit it. John drove on back to Morganton, which is an hour and thirty-seven minutes from here, and I dressed the bird.

When I dressed the bird, I carefully noted what type of shot it had in it and from what direction it had been hit. Every shot in that bird was from John's gun. There was no shot from mine.

I got on the telephone and said, "John, you might as well come on back up here and get this bird, now. It's yours. Every shot in it came from the side that you were shooting from."

John said, "Just put him in the freezer. I'll be back up there next week and I'll pick him up then."

Stories from Big John

Earlier, I had some things to say about the values of grouse hunting. Some things that I didn't mention have to do with the fine stories you can hear from your hunting partner whenever the hunting gets slack, when there's not much going on, or when you sit down to rest for a while, or when you stop for lunch. Some of the stories are worth passing along. One is from Big John, whom I was fortunate enough to have as my hunting partner for twenty-five or thirty years.

In later years, Big John lost part of his hearing ability, not enough to cause him to get a hearing aid, not enough to cause him to stop his grouse hunting, but enough to worry him. We friends of his knew that he was having some problems with his hearing.

Being the fine, friendly fellow Big John is, he has a lot of friends. One of those friends is a gentleman named Clontz. One day Mr. Clontz was going through a flea market in the town of Morganton, North Carolina, and he found what we call an earhorn. I remember that thing as being advertised, I believe, by the Victor Talking Machine Company with a picture of an earhorn plugged into a radio, with a little beagle dog listening in that earhorn.

Well, Mr. Clontz found such a horn. He said, "That is exactly what Big John needs."

This earhorn is small at the end that goes in the ear, of course, and at the other end is as big as the big brass horn that some bands carry around. Mr. Clontz takes this earhorn to Big John. He says, "Buddy, I brought you something."

Big John says, "Good! That's fine! I know exactly what I'll do with that. I can't halfway hear that lady preacher in church. I'll take that thing to church with me. When she starts talking, I'll put that thing in my ear and I'll turn the big end towards her and I'll know exactly what is going on."

The two gentlemen go to church. They take the earhorn. They sit down on the back seat. The service progresses to the point that the lady minister stops to pray. While she is praying, Big John and Mr. Clontz get that earhorn installed in John's ear and turn the big end of it toward the front of the church.

Well, the reverend says her prayer and says, "Amen." She opens her eyes and looks out over the congregation and she sees Big John sitting back there with this earhorn in his ear, and his friend sitting there holding up the big end of it, helping him hold it.

The minister adds a little something to her prayer, "Lord, help us! Amen. Amen."

Big John told me another story that happened in the same church but with a different minister. This minister was a new man who had been sent in by the powers that be that assign ministers. He called a council meeting. He was trying to make improvements, of course, to have a bigger church and more people and better services and so forth.

In his remarks in the council meeting, the new minister said, "I want to build up more interest in this church. I want to get the program a little more animated, a little more lively. I want people to enjoy the service more. I want the whole congregation to be more active, to take more interest in what is going on.

"Now next week is the fifth Sunday in the month. That's the Sunday that the area superintendent visits our church. I'd like to have a good report to give that superintendent."

Big John stood up and said, "Reverend, I have a suggestion that I believe will create some interest in this church. I believe it will cause the people to take a lot more interest, to take a lot more action, and to get a lot more excited about the services here."

The good reverend said, "What's your suggestion?"

Big John replied, "I have a friend who lives on Grandfather Mountain. He makes a living out of catching rattlesnakes up there on the south side—it won't work on the north side—but on the south side, when it gets warm in the spring of the year, he catches rattlesnakes and sells 'em to laboratories here 'n there. My suggestion is that we buy half a dozen rattlesnakes from this gentleman, put 'em in a box, and bring 'em down here and set 'em right in front of your pulpit. I believe on Sunday morning that you'll have a lot of interest. Things will start popping in this church."

The good reverend just looked at Big John for a minute then said, "Would you please go to the back and sit down and keep quiet until we get through here?"

Duck Hunting Tales

In McDowell County, North Carolina, there is a Lake James. It's a lake formed by two rivers running into it: the Catawba River and the Linville River. It's a Duke Power Company impoundment. In the winter time, it's a good duck hunting area, especially below the spillway that empties into the Catawba River, which flows on down through Burke County and eventually into the sea. In the winter time, two friends and I would float a metal canoe on the Catawba River below Lake James and shoot ducks after they flushed off the water.

To get close enough to a duck to shoot it after it flushes off the water, that canoe must float down that river real quiet. You mustn't be making any noise with the paddle, you mustn't be scraping any rocks, you mustn't be talking. The canoe floats down at the same speed as a leaf floating on the water, and we hope as quietly as a leaf floats.

One early morning before daylight we put into the Catawba River below Lake James. It was a cold morning. It was so cold that there was ice on each bank of the river, out for a foot or two. It was cold enough that when you touched your bare hands to that canoe your fingers would freeze to it. Of course, we wore gloves and warm clothing to keep that from happening.

As we floated down the river, we floated by an area that was used by a dredging firm to dredge sand out of the river to sell to customers to build roads and what have you. It just so happened that we drifted by that sand pit operation, that gravel pit operation, about the time that those people would go to work, about eight o'clock. As we drifted in view, a man came from the machinery of the sand and gravel operation, out to the water's edge to get a bucket of water for something, maybe to pour into the radiator of a piece of machinery. He didn't see us. He bent over the water and dipped his bucket in, and as he came back up, the canoe had drifted right toward him. We were within two or three feet of him. He straightened up. Of course, he could hardly believe his eyes. Here on this cold morning in a metal canoe were three men who were big enough fools to go duck hunting.

"You boys have the spirit, don't you," he said.

We said, "Yes sir!" And on down the river we floated.

When we duck hunt like that we have to have two vehicles. We take one vehicle to carry the canoe to the point that we put in the river, and then we have to park a vehicle at the point in the river where we are going to take out. When we take out, we load our canoe onto that vehicle, then go back to the starting point for the other vehicle.

We did that this day. And when we got back to the starting point, we found two of the game wardens, two fellows that were friends of ours, that we knew well. They weren't interested in checking us or trying to arrest us, or anything. They just wanted to borrow our canoe. We told them we would loan it to them.

They wanted to know if we had seen any ducks. We told them, no, we hadn't flushed a duck, hadn't seen a feather. There just wasn't anything on that river that day. Maybe they had gone; maybe they had frozen up. We just hadn't seen a feather.

In blundering around getting the canoe onto their vehicle and getting the life jackets out of our cars, we opened the trunk of one car. In that trunk we had three life jackets plus a bag full of ducks. We had killed something like ten or fifteen, whatever the limit is for ducks given the number of people in our party.

One of those game wardens opened that bag and looked down in it and said, "You sons of bitches! You've killed every duck on the river."

Ray Bryant

I have one brother-in-law, a fine gentlemen, that lives close enough for me to pull jokes on. I think the world of him. Every time I get an opportunity, I pull a trick on him, but I still think an awful lot of him. In the duck hunting segment while ago, where I mentioned loaning the canoe to the game wardens and their finding the bag of ducks—just about all of those ducks were mallards. All but two of them were mallards, but two of them were hooded mergansers.

Now, mallards are a fine, edible duck. Of course, mallards feed on grass and weeds and seeds and so forth, and when fixed properly are just as fine a plate as you can imagine. The hooded merganser is just exactly the opposite. Those mergansers eat fish; that's what they live on. And when you clean one up and cook it, it smells just exactly like a fish that's been out of ice too long. Now, can't any human being eat a hooded merganser.

One of my buddies on that trip asked, "What will we do with the hooded mergansers? Should we throw them away?"

I said, "No. No, let us not throw them away. I have a brother-in-law who has a birthday next week, and he'll be having a birthday dinner and a birthday party. Let's dress those mergansers and fix them up real good and freeze them, and when they're frozen good, I'll take them over to my brother-in-law and tell him with our compliments, both yours and mine, that we have remembered him on his birthday. It is our wish to present him with two fine ducks for his birthday dinner and we hope that he enjoys them."

So we fixed them up and I took them to my brother-in-law.

"Ray," I said, "Charles and John and I have remembered you and have fixed you some ducks. We'd like to know some of these days how you like them."

I gave those hooded mergansers to Ray and his wife, who is my sister. They thanked me profusely for them. I told them it was quite all right, that we'd enjoyed killing them and fixing them and hoped that they'd enjoy eating them.

Now I knew all the time that no human being can eat those ducks. The longer you cook them, the worse they smell, till eventually you have to leave the kitchen or throw them away, one.

A week after Ray's birthday, I saw him and said, "How was your birthday party?"

"Pretty good," he said.

"How did you like those ducks?"

"We haven't fixed those ducks yet. We never did eat them."

To this day I've never found out what he did with them.

Ray is a graduate of North Carolina State University. When he graduated, he came back to Mitchell County as head of the local office of the U.S. Soil and Water Conservation Service. Now that service is a federal department and they work under the Department of Agriculture, and they have a supervisor in each state. Ray Bryant's supervisor was a gentleman in Raleigh.

One day I had a telephone call from Raleigh, from Ray Bryant's supervisor. He said, "I'm coming to Mitchell County next week to work with Ray Bryant some and go around with Ray Bryant some—see what he's been doing, check on some of his work. And I wanted to know if I could come to your house with Ray Bryant and get you to take us to a wildlife planting that I understand you've put out somewhere back in the woods for grouse and for wildlife in general."

I told him, "Yes, it would be fine. It would be all right."

"Well, would it be all right if I bring a shotgun along and maybe do a little grouse hunting while we go through the woods?"

I said that would be fine, just show up at my house about nine o'clock in the morning, something like that. So we set the date; I believe it was on a Friday. I notified one of my regular grouse hunting partners of what was coming up, so when the party came, there were four of us.

Well, Ray Bryant is not a hunter. He doesn't want any part of hunting. He realized that day he might be getting into something that just wouldn't be a lot of satisfaction to him. So Ray said, "I believe I'll drive my vehicle behind you fellas, so when I get ready to come home, I can come home. Then I don't have to go on with you fellas if I don't want to go."

I said that would be fine, so we drove two vehicles as far as we could drive them and parked them. We got our lunches out; we hunters put our lunches in our game bags, and Ray Bryant carried his in a paper bag in his hand.

We started up through the mountains grouse hunting, moving toward the wildlife planting, but we weren't seeing any grouse. After about an hour of that I looked over to a mountain to the west of us and said, "Now last week, I saw some birds on that mountain over there. It's not more than thirty minutes to it. Let's go over there and see what we can find."

Ray said, "You're not going over *there*, are you?"

I said, "Yea. It's a good place to go. Go with us."

"Naw. I'm not going. I'll sit right down beside this pine tree and rest. I'll be right here when you fellas come back."

We left Ray sitting by a pine tree, a big white pine tree.

We were gone an hour and a half, probably. When we came back, Ray was sitting by the pine tree right where we had left him, but he had eaten his lunch. He said, "Now I've had enough of this. I believe I'll go back home and you fellas can go on and have a good time. But I've had enough of it. I'm going back."

He looked at my friend John and said, "John, which way do I go to get to my truck?"

John said, "Ray, you go west right here. West, right down through yonder."

I said, "No. No, Ray. You don't go that way. John's telling you wrong. You go east. You go *that* way."

He couldn't believe either one of us. Neither of us was telling him right, of course. He should have gone some other way, and he knew we were telling him wrong, so he trudged along with us all day long.

To this day, Ray Bryant says, "You'll never get me out in the woods with you again. That taught me one lesson. I'll never go out with you fellas anymore!"

While I've got Ray Bryant on my mind, I've got one more story, then we'll let him rest in peace.

Now Ray has an office in the little town of Bakersville. He works five days a week, from roughly eight o'clock to five. In addition to being the Soil Conservation man and having an office in Bakersville, Ray owns about two hundred acres of land not too far from me. On that two hundred acres of land are a lot of grouse, and those grouse don't get hunted because Ray Bryant won't let you hunt. The only way we can hunt them is to get Ray Bryant out of town and hunt them before he gets back.

For years I tried to put together a situation where Ray Bryant would be in Raleigh for a week at the time the grouse season was open, but it seemed like that never did happen. One day, we decided to try something else. It was a good day to go grouse hunting, so I called my buddy to tell him to come on up and we'd go. If we could work it out, we'd hunt Ray Bryant's grouse. Ray Bryant had a lot of grouse because they didn't get shot much, and they needed to be stirred up and mixed around a little for survival, to get their genes mixed up with other birds so as not to inbreed too much. Now Ray doesn't believe that, but that's right.

My buddy came on up and I said I'd have to find out where Ray was. I called Ray's office and he answered the telephone. I said, "Ray, how do you feel today?"

"Fine."

"What's your schedule today?"

"I've got to do this and I've got to do that."

"Well, when you have time, I'd like you to do a little something for me. I just thought I'd let you know to put me on your schedule sometime in the next week or two." I thought I pulled it off pretty smooth, but evidently Ray smelled a mouse.

My buddy and I went on past Ray's house and went grouse hunting back in his woods. I don't know how many times we shot, how many grouse we killed, but we had a ball. It was just bang-bang-bang. We were having a lot of grouse, the dogs were pointing, a lot of activity.

It came time to get out of there. We had to give ourselves some safety margin. Now we thought that Ray got out of the office about five o'clock, so we gave ourselves an hour's safety margin and quit at four o'clock to get by Ray's house and get gone before he came in. So we came on down and pulled our game bags off and put our guns in the truck and loaded up our dogs and got in the truck and started to go on down the road.

To get to my home, you have to go right by Ray Bryant's home. We got just about to Ray Bryant's house, when lo and behold there stood Ray Bryant, right there in the middle of the road, with a stick in his hand and grinning. We pulled on down.

He said, "All right, get out of there! Get out of that truck and just stand right over here. I'm going to teach you boys a lesson."

Later on, I tried to give Ray two of those grouse. I believe the following Thanksgiving I knocked on his door and he came to the door. I said, "Ray, do you remember those grouse John and I killed up here on your property?"

"Remember! I won't ever forget it!"

"Well, here are two of them. I brought them for you for Thanksgiving dinner."

"Now you're just trying to bribe me. I'll take 'em, but I want you to understand that doesn't mean I'm giving you permission to go back in there and grouse hunt any more."

In addition to Ray Bryant, I have one other brother-in-law, named Earl Harbour. He lives in the town of Cameron, in Moore County, North Carolina. Earl is a fine fellow. Personality wise, he is a combination of the Reverend Billy Graham, singer Tennessee Ernie Ford, and storyteller Jerry Clower. Anytime you have a day to spare and want to hear good stories and jokes, Earl Harbour can entertain you.

Skoal Tobacco

One Saturday a geological engineer I knew from the city of Atlanta (he was raised in Bakersville but he had a job in Atlanta with some firm down there) came up to go grouse hunting with me. We hunted all day and had some success. He's a real pleasant fellow.

The fact that Mr. Blevins was a geological engineer wasn't the outstanding feature about Mr. Blevins on the grouse hunt. What was outstanding about Mr. Blevins on the grouse hunt was the amount of Skoal tobacco he kept in his mouth during that whole grouse hunt. Skoal tobacco comes in a little tin can about as big as a flat biscuit, I guess, and it has a real fragrant wintergreen aroma to it, a flavor. All that day I thoroughly enjoyed the aroma from Mr. Blevins's Skoal tobacco that he had in his mouth.

He didn't chew that tobacco like you would chew a plug of tobacco. He just put it in his mouth and as far as I could tell held it on the tip of his tongue. He was spitting all day long. Every time he spit, that Skoal tobacco smelled real good.

We were driving his vehicle that day. On our way back out of the woods, I decided that I ought to try some of that Skoal tobacco.

He handed me the tin and said, "Just get a tiny pinch, 'cause a little bit goes a long way. Just get a tiny pinch and don't chew it between your teeth. Pull your lower lip away from your teeth and put that Skoal right back inside your mouth between your cheek and your lower teeth and let it stay there."

I followed instructions and put the tobacco inside my mouth after we got back in the truck and started back down the road.

In about two minutes I had to spit from that Skoal tobacco. I rolled the window down and spit outside the window with no problem. In two minutes I had to spit again. I spit outside the window. In a few more minutes I had to spit again. By the third time I noticed that my spitting wasn't quite as efficient as it was the first time. I was beginning to see double a little bit, which was affecting my ability to spit. I kept trying to spit outside the window but I wasn't doing a good job. I was doing such a poor job that part of it was blowing back in the cab on us.

I figured the thing to do was not to try to spit out the window any more but just to open the truck door the least bit and lean down and spit out right down beside the fender, in the road. I did that ten or fifteen times, going on down the road. After awhile I got to where I was afraid to open the door. I was afraid I might open it too wide and fall out. I was just losing control.

I told Mr. Blevins, "You watch along the side of this road, and if you see a can of any kind—a plastic can, a beer can, just a can of any kind—would you stop and let me get it. I'll bring it in here and spit in it, 'cause I'm getting in trouble. I can't spit out the window, and I can't spit out the door. If I had a can, I'd hold it to my mouth and spit directly into it."

After awhile he saw a beer can, so he pulled over and stopped, and I got out and went to get the beer can. It was at the side of an area where they had been loading logs, so it was a pretty wide area, between the truck and the shoulder of the road. I went and got my beer can and for the life of me I couldn't walk back to that truck. I got down on my hands and knees, and I held my beer can up in one hand, and I crawled from where I picked up the can back to the truck and crawled into the truck.

My good friend said, "All I need now is a camera. I can run your picture in the paper with this caption: 'Here's a member of the board of education, not only a member but the chairman of the board of education, so drunk on beer that he couldn't even walk back to the truck but crawled on his hands and knees.'"

We've had many a laugh out of that episode. I told my wife all about that. She didn't think it was too funny. But, I finally found me a can to spit in.

How to Fry Good Country Ham

In the late 1970s, a friend of mine who lives in Fairfield County, South Carolina, at a little crossroads named Salem Crossroads, invited my oldest boy, Doug, and me to come down to his farm (they had enough acres for a plantation, practically) to go turkey hunting with him. We accepted the invitation.

We decided to make a camper out of my Jeep, put the camper top on it and take a Coleman lantern and Coleman stove, and food, and all the necessities for camping out in the woods for a period of two or three days.

On our drive down, just inside the South Carolina line, we stopped at a grocery store that had a sign out front, Cured Country Hams for Sale. The name if that grocery store was Coles Grocery Store. I went into that store and bought a country ham that weighed twenty-three pounds.

We drove on down to Salem Crossroads and met our friend. He showed us a good place to camp. We set up camp and cooked our evening meal on an open fire made out of limbs gathered from the woods. In addition to the light from the fire, we hung a lantern from the limb of a tree, far enough away from the fire that there wouldn't be any danger of the lantern fuel catching fire. We ate our evening meal and sat around the fire and laughed and told tales and enjoyed everybody's company.

In addition to the friend who had given us the invitation, another gentleman that we knew and who lived in the area came to our camp fire that night and visited with us awhile. He said, "Just at dark tonight, just about five to ten miles from here, I heard a turkey gobbler go to roost. I'll take one of you fellows over there in the morning and help you find that turkey. I'll come back here an hour before daylight, and I'll take whichever of you wants to go."

We got up the next morning, probably about five o'clock, and started cooking breakfast. There were four people in the camp, who cooked breakfast together, Doug, myself, James Miller (who we had taken from here), and the man that had invited us. We made a big pot of coffee. We cut that country ham I had bought, and we put it in a frying pan that we had brought that was about twice the size of the normal frying pan that you would use in the kitchen. That frying pan was about eighteen inches in diameter, about eighteen inches across.

We cut up enough pieces of that country ham to put into that frying pan to cover the entire surface of the pan. We cooked the pan of meat on the open fire there. We had anther pan the same size that we were scrambling some eggs in. It just so happened that the pan of meat got cooked and got done before the eggs did. We started cooking the meat first, and it got done first.

Whoever was cooking the meat set it down on the ground just at the edge of the light from the camp fire, not in real good light, just in the shadows, opposite of where the lantern was hanging. The fire was between the lantern and the pan of meat.

One man was cooking the eggs, and someone was making the coffee. I don't know what I was doing; it sounds like nothing. But I was sitting fairly close to where that pan of meat was set down.

About that time came the gentleman who was going to show us where he had heard the turkey the night before. He didn't come to eat with us, I don't believe. He had eaten breakfast at home. He got there before we ate, and he was standing there with his hands crossed, talking with us.

He was standing close to me. I looked around and I thought, "Well, he's standing pretty close to where that pan of meat is." I asked one of the fellows to bring the lantern over so I could do a little looking. When he brought that lantern over, I shined it around to my right.

Our friend's foot was placed completely in that pan of fried meat. Of course he didn't know it. He was standing there with his arms folded across his chest, visiting with us, with his right foot in the frying pan, on that fine country ham that we had set back there to cool a little bit.

It didn't take long to decide what to do. We decided the thing to do was to look at his shoe real carefully to see how dirty it was, to see how nasty.

It didn't look too bad. We got our pan of meat up and turned each piece over, set the pan back on the camp fire, reheated it, then ate that whole pan of meat.

There was general agreement that the meat tasted a little better than usual. It just could be that a little bit of barnyard acid added a little zip, a little zing to that ham that it would not otherwise have.

Turkey Hunting with James Miller

I went to South Carolina turkey hunting on several different trips with James Miller, one of the fine sons of a splendid neighbor, Lester Miller. After four or five of those trips, I had killed a turkey or two, but James had not been lucky enough to get one.

On one trip we broke camp just before daylight and went down to the Little River in South Carolina, found a trail that headed north up the river, and started hiking. After hiking for thirty minutes, we heard turkey gobblers sounding off on the right, which would have been on the east. The turkeys were about one or two hundred yards from the trail we were on, and they were strung out on a ridge line that was covered with long-leaf pine trees.

We stood and listened to those turkeys gobble, probably, for ten minutes. To the best of our estimation there were either seven or eight of them. They weren't gobbling from the same location, but they were all gobbling from the same ridge line.

I said, "Now James, you haven't killed a turkey yet, and I have, so those seven or eight turkeys are yours. You go over there and see what you can do with them. I'll keep on heading north and I'll meet you back here in about three or four hours, right at this same spot where we're standing right now."

A.D. Harrell and James Miller with a turkey.

I headed north and walked for an hour and a half or maybe two hours. I didn't hear any turkeys. Incidentally, I didn't hear James shoot, either, so I was apprehensive as to whether or not he had done any good. I turned around and I started back to the location where he and I had separated.

When I came to the point where James and I had separated earlier, I stopped. I put my turkey call in my mouth, not to call a turkey, but to call real loud to let James know that I was back and that I would be waiting for him. When I made three notes on that turkey call, trying to call to James, a turkey gobbler gobbled right back at me. That turkey gobbler was within twenty-five yards of me. I'd hunted turkeys enough to know and recognize a gobble that was real intense, with the turkey probably going straight to my call.

I had my gloves off. I had my mask off. I didn't have anything ready. I said to myself, "You'd better get ready in a hurry, 'cause that turkey's coming out of there."

I stepped in behind a head-high cedar bush and put my camouflage gloves on and put my mask on my face; didn't call another

time, just stood behind that cedar bush, watching. In about a m-
inute and a half, here come one of the biggest turkey gobblers I'd
ever seen, right out of the woods. He stopped right in the trail in
front of my cedar bush and went to strutting.

I raised my gun and lowered the boom on him. He fell there in
the road and went to fluttering. He was a fine turkey.

I don't recall if that turkey had quit fluttering or not till James
Miller came crawling out of the brush. He pulled his mask off and
looked at me and said, "A.D., you shot my turkey."

The Slave Cemetery

From Whitmire, South Carolina, if you travel north on Highway
176, about a mile or two out of Whitmire, on the left, you will come
to Highway 18 South. That highway leads you into the Sumter National Forest area. If you continue on Highway 18 South in a western direction, you will come to Interstate 26 at a village called Cross
Anchors.

Now backing up a bit, when you get on Highway 18 South, traveling west, you come to a Forest Service road that in 1978 or '79
was numbered 340. This road runs south for about six miles, down
to the Enoree River. At the end of Forest Service Road 340, I set up
camp one night, right on the banks of the Enoree River.

About an hour before dark, our son Doug joined me. He had
flown from Greensboro, North Carolina, down to Columbia, South
Carolina, and had rented a car and had driven out to my camp site.
He and I had prearranged where we would camp, so he knew
where I would be.

He came out and camped with me. The next morning, we got up and turkey hunted for a few hours, then Doug had to go back to Columbia, get on his plane, and go back to his job.

After Doug left, I was hiking through the woods somewhere along the Enoree River, about nine o'clock in the morning. I had hiked as far as I wanted to hike and was circling back towards camp. I was in a forest of long-leaf pines, and the trees averaged about twenty-four inches in diameter at about breast high to a man. It was National Forest Service land, looked after by the U.S. Department of Agriculture, the U.S. Forest Service.

Out in these trees, about one-hundred-fifty yards from where I was standing, I saw what appeared to be a turkey blind, that I assumed some hunter had built. It appeared to be an enclosure that was about three feet high. I could see it quite clearly because the Forest Service, a year or two prior to that time, had had a controlled burn there. That is a burn in which the Forest Service burns out the underbrush and the tangles and so forth under the big trees. It's good for the big trees, and it's also good for wildlife in that it allows new growth to come and produce seeds that the wildlife, particularly quail and turkey and so forth, will use. In this forest, the floor was clean, and you could see for quite a distance.

I saw this structure out in front. I believed that I should go look at that structure. I wanted to see what kind of blind somebody had built. I walked over to this structure, and I was completely surprised by what I found.

The structure had been build completely over a grave. It had been built of two gray granite blocks about nine feet long and about fourteen inches in height and about four inches thick. There were two granite blocks on each side, and there were two granite blocks on each end. The granite blocks on the end were abut three feet wide and otherwise the same dimensions and the same color as the longer blocks. Those large granite blocks would each weigh about a ton in my opinion.

They were built up to make the structure in the same engineering pattern that a brick mason would use to build a chimney. They weren't put together with any mortar of any kind. They were mortised or laid together in the same pattern that you would use to build a brick chimney, and they were supporting each other. On the east side of that structure, one of those big stones, the bottom one, had been pried away, pulled away, in an obvious attempt to vandalize the grave.

This structure was about the height of a dining room table. On top of it, covering the entire structure, was a piece of solid gray granite about an inch thick, nine feet long, and three feet wide.

On further investigation, it was barely visible that the entire surface was covered with old English carving that was difficult to read. It had clearly been there as long as the trees that were standing beside it, and there were trees standing near that structure ranging from two to three feet through. The writing was covered with debris that had fallen from the trees, from the bark, and from the storms over the years. It was covered with droppings from the birds. It was covered with lichen that had grown up on the surface of that gray granite.

I took my handkerchief and I brushed and I brushed and I brushed. Then I broke some limbs off the trees and I brushed all I could, to see if I could read the writing. I was able to read some of it. One line started out, "Captain Bernard Glenn," and it gave his date of birth and his date of death. Another line clearly was, "In the state of Virginia, the County of Cumberland, date . . ."; 1860 something, I believe.

I worked some on the third line, where I read something that indicated this fellow had been in the South Carolina state militia, and the timing of his service, I assumed, was in the Civil War.

When I was trying to read the Old English writing, I was reading with the sun about half high, about nine o'clock, with the sun coming out of the east, shining through the trees. The sun's rays can mess up the reading with shadows and the rays and so forth. But I read what I could, and I went on back to camp and thought about what I had found.

During my lunch, I decided that if I go back to that structure at three o'clock in the evening, the sun's rays will be coming from a different direction, and I'll be able to read a little bit more.

So, I went back around three o'clock. I don't remember that I could read a great deal more, but I found something that really aroused my interest. I saw that the granite structure was in the apparent middle of a big cemetery. Standing some hundred yards west of the granite structure, with the sun's rays shining just exactly right, I could see row after row of graves on either side of that structure. I guessed that there were a hundred or more graves there, and they were aligned real clearly from an east-west direction, till I could look down the line and at each place see a sunken area where whatever type of coffin that had been used had finally disintegrated and the grave had sunk.

On further investigation, I saw that the Forest Service had protected this cemetery in their controlled burning. They had used a bulldozer to construct a fire lane around this cemetery. The undergrowth and the brush within the cemetery was still there, while the area outside of the cemetery had been cleared.

Here, deep within the forest on the Enoree River, I had found an unusual cemetery.

The trees told me that the last person buried in that cemetery was buried at least seventy-five and probably ninety years earlier. I've been outdoors all my life, and when I cut down a big tree, I count the rings and determine when there have been droughts by the size of the rings. During periods of dry weather, those growth rings are real close together. During periods of wet weather, those growth rings are big and fairly wide apart. So, I knew from the size of those trees that I was looking at a cemetery that nobody had cared for, other than the Forest Service not burning it over, in the past seventy-five or ninety years.

In my driving around the area, I observed that there was no house closer than ten miles to that cemetery. I didn't know what I had found, but I thought and thought about it that night while I was camping by myself. I theorized that it was probably created in conjunction with a prisoner of war camp for the Civil War.

My theory was that the people buried in that cemetery were soldiers, the prisoners of war from the camp. My theory further said that probably some father who lived in Virginia in the 1860s to '80s knew that his son had died in a prisoner of war camp on the Enoree River, outside of Whitmire. That this father in his love for his son had come to the cemetery and determined in which one of those graves lay his son. My further theory was that this father spent what time and effort was necessary to have the granite monument built over the grave of the son who had died during the Civil War. Now, that was the theory I came up with. It was a theory that tugged at your heart and that satisfied me.

The next morning after I had put this theory together, in my hiking in the general area I came across a herd of cattle a mile or so down the river from the camp. These were beef cattle that were fenced in an open pasture. As I walked by that pasture, I saw a mother cow giving birth to a calf, and she was clearly in trouble. She was having a difficult delivery, and it was clear she needed some help. I saw nobody. I had seen nobody, apart from Doug, at all during the two days and nights I was in the area.

I decided to help the animal. She was so far along that she had laid down, and I could approach her without her getting up. I laid my gun down and went to her and helped her deliver that calf. Then, I went on about my way.

Sometime later that day I was driving out from camp on my way home. I met a black man who was walking, and I stopped and visited with him.

He asked, "Are you hunting by yourself?"

"Yes. I am."

"Well, I've noticed you here for two or three days, and I haven't seen anyone with you. I'm the herdsman for the cattle down here, so I decided that every day I would check on you and see if you were getting along all right. There are some snakes in this area, and a man by himself might fall and get hurt or something, so I decided to check on you."

I told him that I had seen the cattle that morning, and that I had helped one of his cows deliver a calf. Of course, that made friends out of us, and we visited awhile. He got in my truck, and sat down and we talked at some length.

I told him about my cemetery find. I said, "Do you know anything about that?"

"Yes. Yes, I do."

"Tell me. Tell me what you know."

This is what he told me: A hundred years ago this was a cotton plantation. These big pine trees are on land that at one time were areas that grew cotton. A man had come down here from some place in Virginia and had a hundred or so slaves. He tilled all these river flood plain areas in cotton and tended it with his slaves. The man's name was Glenn, as I had read on the granite.

The story goes that sometime in the early 1800s, he set aside this area of land for a slave cemetery. In the very center of the cemetery, he set aside a twelve-foot plot. He said in his will that he wanted to be buried in that twelve-foot plot, in the midst of the people who had worked for him for so long. He outlined the type

The granite structure over the grave of Captain Bernard Glenn, along the Enoree River in South Carolina.

of structure to be built over his grave, and that was the structure I had found.

After I visited with the black man, and he told me about the cemetery, about the slaves and the white master who was buried in their midst and about the cotton fields and so forth, I told him I was leaving. I went down to the village of Whitmire. At a cafe, named Miller's Cafe, I went in to eat lunch.

I was a little late for lunch, about quarter of one. When I went in, all of the tables were taken. There were some twenty tables in that cafe, with four chairs at each table, and they were all taken. I walked in, in my hunting clothes, and stood around for half a minute, looking for a place to sit down. Across the way, I saw three business men from the area having lunch. When we made eye contact, one of them motioned for me to come over and take the empty chair at their table. I went over and sat down and introduced myself, and they told me who they were. We talked a little, and I ordered my meal.

They wanted to know if I was turkey hunting, and I said yes. They wanted to know where, so I told them where I was located. They wanted to know if I was by myself, and I told them that I was, except for the one night that my son was with me. They said that I shouldn't be out there by myself because it is a real snaky area. Then, they started telling me snake tales.

I understood real quick that they were embellishing these snake tales with the idea of maybe shaking me up or getting me concerned about hunting out there. They weren't doing it out of antagonism, but just in a friendly manner. But they told me some real big snake tales about how many rattle snakes there were per acre along the Enoree River and that the snakes in the eastern side, along which I was hunting, were bigger than the snakes on the western side. All kinds of snake tales.

Well, that exchange of stories and tales went on until they had about finished their meals. When they had finished their meals and they had finished their snake tales, I said, "Order yourselves another cup of coffee, because I want to tell you one, too. I'll give you a North Carolina version."

We each ordered more coffee, and I told them this:

I have a friend in Columbus County, North Carolina, down on the coast. Right close to where that friend lives is what is known as the Green River Swamp, a part of a river basin that is part of an estuary. (The ocean backs up in there, too.) It is an isolated area. A lot of it is public land, I understand, with no state-maintained roads in much of it.

This friend of mine was driving an old Jeep road one morning, looking at plantings for quail. He had been in the area the evening before, going up and down the same road that he was on. This morning, when he was three miles away from home on this road, he came to a tree that had fallen across the road in the night. He got out to look at it. It was small enough to tempt a man to try to move it, but he decided it was just a little bit too big, that he'd better go back to the house and get a power saw and cut it into lengths that he could handle without possibly hurting his back, then get it out of the way and go on by.

He goes back home and gets his power saw. He drives back to the log and gets his power saw out of the vehicle and sets it down beside the log. He pulls three or four times on that string on the power saw that you use to start it with, and finally the power saw starts running. He revs it up to a real large whine and gets ready to saw that log in two. He sets the saw up on the log and lets the teeth come down on the bark and opens it all the way open, until it roars like only a chain saw can roar. That tree starts moving!

My friend backed off and watched while that tree just crawled off, down into the swamp.

"Now, gentlemen," I said, "that's a North Carolina snake tale for you!"

On October 25, 1994, I took my wife, Geneva, and our daughter, Rose Marie, and her husband, Tony Johnson, to Sumter National Forest. After a search of some thirty minutes, I relocated this slave cemetery. We took a steel brush and cleaned off the debris and so forth on the writing on the granite cover on the large granite structure. We were able to read the entire writing on that granite slab. This is what the writing was:

To the memory of Captain Bernard Glenn who departed this life the 8th day of August 1831 in the 74th year of his age. He was born in the state of Virginia, Cumberland County, the 26th day of February 1757. At an early age he embarked in the struggle of his country for independence and served as an officer until the close of the Revolution with honor to himself and usefulness to his country. He afterwards removed to South Carolina and was by the spontaneous voice of his fellow citizens repeatedly called to preside in the councils of the state, where he was distinguished alike for his patriotism, sound judgment, and spotless integrity. His latter days were spent in retirement on his farm, beloved and respected by all for his honesty, humanity, and benevolence.

The New Gun

To many upland bird hunters the Browning over and under, the premium grade of that gun, is the finest shotgun that anyone can hunt with. Three times in my grouse hunting years, and that's sixty-five years, I've hunted with a partner that carried a Browning over and under. On those occasions my partner let me handle his gun, I put it to my shoulder, I sighted down the barrel, I swung it at imaginary targets, but I did not fire the gun.

I asked each of those three men what the gun cost. When I was told the cost, my mind and my common sense said, No way. To a man who had grown up in the depression of the '20s and '30s, that was too much money to put in a gun. I'd had such a difficult time getting enough money to get through high school and finally through college that my conscience tended to say, "You ought to shoot a sling shot, made out of a forked stick and two pieces of inner tube rubber, with a piece of leather to hold the projectile. That might be more appropriate than buying any kind of shotgun."

Down through the years I shot guns in this order: a model 97 Winchester pump, a model 59 Winlight with a fiberglass barrel, and I am now in 1995 shooting a Franchie. Those last two guns are semi-automatic and are still in excellent condition, so I don't really need a new gun.

I number in the hundreds the grouse I've killed with each of those guns. When I consider the hunter competition, I doubt if any man will kill as many grouse as I have collected. I don't think anyone will have the chances I've had. It must be said that each of those grouse made someone a fine meal, if not for my family, then a meal for some neighbor in the area.

In late years at Christmas time, my wife and children are forever asking me, "Daddy, what do you want for Christmas?"

My answer is, "I don't know of anything I need, but if you want to buy me that Browning over and under shotgun . . . "

That's about as far as I ever get with that sentence before I get the answer loud and clear, "Forget it!"

Now I know it is written, "Don't put new wine in old containers," and "You cannot teach an old dog new tricks." And someone has probably said, "An old man can't shoot a new shotgun."

With all due respect to and in spite of all the philosophy expressed in the paragraph above, in the seventy-eighth year of this fine life I decided to buy that Browning over and under shotgun. I took my wife, Geneva, with me. We went to Johnson City, Tennessee, and went to the finest outdoor store in this general area and looked at the Browning over and under that I wanted. We asked prices and talked with the man to see what was the least that he would take. Well, I didn't buy the gun.

We came home and that night I called our son, Larry, in Charlotte, North Carolina, and told him what kind of gun I wanted to buy. I asked him if he would take a little time off and see what he could find in the Charlotte area and get back to me with some kind of report on it.

In a day or two Larry called back and said, "Daddy, I have found that shotgun. I can get it here for you for about three or four hundred dollars less than the man in Johnson City was asking for it. What do you want me to do?"

"Go ahead and pick it up. I'll put you a check in the mail tomorrow."

A day later Larry called back and said, "I have the gun. I'll be up there this coming Friday with it."

Friday rolled around. Larry came and brought the gun. I was just tickled pink with it.

Larry and I decided to take that gun and his gun and go out grouse hunting for awhile. Out to the woods we went, but before we had a chance to shoot either gun, the dog we go hunting with, a Brittany named Rusty, ran across some glass or something and got a severe cut on a front foot. We looked at the dog and decided he was bleeding too heavily to continue. We brought the dog and came on back home, so we didn't have an opportunity to shoot.

The next day I took a crow call that I have and walked out on the hillside near here and called in some crows. A crow came over, quite high.

I thought, "That is about the highest that I ever have shot at anything but I believe I'll try it. I want to shoot this gun. I'm just itchin' to shoot this gun, so I believe I'll try that high crow."

I put the barrel on that crow, swung it out in front if it about five feet, and pulled the trigger. To my complete elation, that crow came tumbling down.

In about two or three minutes, here came three or four crows across, a little bit higher than the first one I shot. I picked out one of those and killed it.

I had it made. I had shot my new gun twice and hit both times.

I reloaded and called up some more crows. A group came over about fifteen feet higher than the others I had shot at. I shot at two of these and didn't hit either one of them, but I knew that I was getting at the extreme limit of the gun's range at that time, which was probably why I didn't kill them.

Two days later, I had an opportunity to shoot at a grouse. The grouse came up on my right and came across from right to left, out at about forty yards. I shot and killed the grouse. Killed it stone dead. The dog went out and retrieved it and brought it to me.

A week later, I went out grouse hunting again with that gun. A bird came off of a limb about a hundred yards up the valley in front of me and came barrelling down the valley right over my head. That is a fairly hard shot, but I brought my gun up and got in front of the bird and pulled the trigger. The bird fell. It fell so close to me that all I had to do was take two steps backward and reach down and pick it up.

I had broken in my new gun. I was real happy and pleased with my crow shots and with the two grouse I had killed. I figured that I had me a gun that maybe an old man could hunt with.

On the Sunday after I got this new gun on Friday, my family and I went to church, the Brethren church here on Harrell Hill. As usual, the wife of our minister had the children come up on the front seat, and she told them some story associated with Christian living and Christian ideals and so forth.

Her name is Berdene Freeman, and Berdene does a super job with those children's stories. She gets the attention not only of the children, but also of us adults, who strain forward and listen intently to every word of her story.

Now on this Sunday after I got my gun on Friday, Berdene's story was this: Some grandmother had broken some of the dishes that went with an eight-piece place setting for her table. The grandmother, being too old to drive, called one of her daughters to take her to town and let her pick out a set of dishes to replace those that had been broken.

The daughter, with her children, come sometime in midweek. They go to town. They find a store that sells dishes, and grandmother finds a set of dishes almost identical to the ones she wants to replace—a beautiful set of dishes, a little finer than the ones they were to replace. They were just exactly what she wanted.

Grandmother bragged on the dishes. She told her family how much she liked them. She told the clerk how much she liked them. But they cost seventy-five dollars.

Without any explanation, Grandmother said, "Let's look at some other places."

They went to some other places that sold dishes. In one of those other places, Grandmother found a set of dishes pretty much the same design as the ones that cost seventy-five dollars, but they were only twenty-five dollars and definitely of an inferior quality to the ones that cost seventy-five. Grandmother spent a little time thinking over the situation and wound up buying that twenty-five dollar set of dishes.

She bought the twenty-five dollar set, although she didn't like them especially, instead of the seventy-five dollar set that she really liked.

On the way back home, one of the grandchildren said, "Grandmother, why did you buy that twenty-five dollar set when you didn't like them really as well as the ones for seventy-five dollars? Why didn't you buy what you wanted?"

Grandmother's answer was, "I knew that if I bought the twenty-five dollar set instead of the seventy-five dollar set, that I would save fifty dollars. I could take that fifty dollars and get out in the community and help some needy family. That's the reason I bought the twenty-five dollar set."

When Berdene finished this story, I leaned over to our son Doug and said, "There goes my new shotgun! I didn't need the shotgun to start with."

Everybody in my pew heard that remark and got a chuckle out of it. When church was over and we went to the door to shake hands with the preacher and his wife, I said, "Berdene, you ruined my new shotgun."

"I did what?"

"You just simply ruined my new shotgun," I said and let it go at that.

The following Sunday, after I had killed the crows and killed the grouse with the gun, I spoke to Berdene about the gun again.

"Today, I can tell you that you are out of the doghouse, because I took that new shotgun out and I did kill some grouse with it, so you are home free."

This new gun is Browning's Citori lightweight, twenty-gauge shotgun, with twenty-four"inch barrels and three interchangeable choke tubes that give me a choice of an improved cylinder, modified, or full-choke barrels. It weighs a little over five pounds.

I know some fine people who, when they go shopping, shop with the idea that if I see something that I may need sometime in the years to come, then I'll buy it now and store it away until I do need it. That idea has caused some arguments in my family in the fifty-two years that we have been a family. All of my married life, until I bought this new shotgun, I've counseled my family, "Don't buy anything unless you need it now. Don't be buying something just because it's on sale. An item that we don't need isn't a bargain, no matter what kind of sale it's on or how much it's reduced."

As far as I can recall, this shotgun is the first pure luxury item I've ever purchased.

CHAPTER FOUR

The Toe River Valley Area

The episodes related in this book occurred mostly on the Toe River Valley in western North Carolina. The Toe River Valley lies between the Blue Ridge Mountains on the east and the Unaka Mountains on the west. The ridge line of the Unaka Mountains is the boundary between the states of Tennessee and North Carolina. The ridge line of the Blue Ridge Mountains is the eastern United States continental divide; water on the eastern side of those mountains flows into the Atlantic Ocean and water on the western side, where the Toe River Valley is, flows into the Gulf of Mexico.

The geopolitical entities in this Toe River Valley are most of Avery County, all of Mitchell County, and all of Yancey County. These three counties are drained by the North Toe and South Toe rivers. The drainage system is called the North Toe River from far up in Avery County until it reaches a point between Kona and Boonford, northwest of Spruce Pine, where it joins the South Toe River. From there on, the river is known as the Toe River. When that Toe River reaches the Tennessee line, below the community of Poplar in Mitchell County, the name is changed to the Nolichucky. The river is called the Nolichucky from the North Carolina-Tennessee line until it flows into one of the Tennessee Valley Authority lakes. That water eventually reaches the Tennessee River, then the Mississippi River, and then the Gulf of Mexico. The Toe River Valley is one of the few watersheds in North Carolina that flows into the Gulf of Mexico; most of the watersheds in the state flow into the Atlantic Ocean.

Most of the terrain in the Toe River Valley is quite steep. It varies anywhere from about a two percent slope to about a seventy percent slope. Quite a bit of it is so steep that a man can barely climb up it. It's like climbing a ladder. Some of the flood plains on the small streams and on the Toe River itself are level enough for mechanical agricultural operations, but not a great deal of land in this Toe River Valley is suitable for any type of agricultural operation that requires machinery. The steepness of the land may be one reason why the growing of Christmas trees is important in the valley. They can be grown without a lot of tractor or machine work.

When I was a young man, the major crops grown on agricultural land in this Toe River Valley were corn, oats, wheat, potatoes, beans, and garden vegetables. There was no such thing as a welfare program. People who needed to eat found a job and went to work. People in town who couldn't find jobs there came out to the farm, rented a place to live, went to work on the farm, and raised enough vegetables and garden crops to provide for the family.

At one time on my father's farm were four different sets of tenants, most of whom came out of the cities to find enough work and to grow enough food to support them and their families. That arrangement lasted until 1932 or '33 and the next few years. Those families that came out of the cities to work on the farm began to go back to the cities because it eventually became clear that they might be better off drawing welfare checks than they would be here on the farm growing food for themselves and their families.

The land ownership is divided into two main categories. One category is ownership by the federal government. This public land is administered by the U.S. Department of Agriculture, with its subhead, the U.S. Forest Service. The rest of the land is under private ownership, and it is broken up into small farms. I'm not sure what the average-sized farm in Mitchell County is, but I would say about fifteen to twenty acres.

Not many farms are large enough to be an independent economic unit able to support a family on its own. Many people do a little work on the farm, such as gardening and growing tobacco, Irish potato patches, bean patches, and so forth, supplemented by work in another industry. Many of our people work in the Spruce Pine area in some of the industries there, and some several of them work as far away as McDowell County or Caldwell County, in industries such as the Baxter Corporation plant in North Cove and the American Thread plant at Sevier.

In relation to the ownership of land, there is a mineral rights situation of interest. Some seventy-five or a hundred years ago, a corporation from Bristol, Tennessee-Virginia, by the name of the Iron Mountain Coal and Steel Works Incorporated (that name may not be exact, but that's about it) owned the mineral rights on land within an area defined like this on the first page of the deed:

> Starting on a corner that is a corner jointly with the County of Mitchell, the County of Avery, and the State of Tennessee, on the crest of a ridgeline at the headwaters of Little Rock Creek, then proceeding down the waters of Little Rock Creek until it runs into Big Rock Creek, then down the waters of Big Rock Creek until it runs into the Toe River, on down the Toe River until it comes to the Tennessee State line, then following in a northeastern direction the Tennessee line along the ridgeline of the Unaka and Iron mountains back to the starting point.

The Iron Mountain Steel Works Corporation sold their mineral rights to the Reynolds family of Bristol. As years passed, the Reynolds family stopped paying taxes on these mineral rights and eventually became a delinquent taxpayer.

In a process worked out with the supervisor of Mitchell County taxes, those mineral rights were acquired by several citizens of Mitchell County. Through working with the tax assessor and tax supervisor and knowing the fact that the Reynoldses had not paid taxes on those mineral rights, those mineral rights were bought up by about ten or twelve men in Mitchell County.

The complete deed for those mineral rights is some fifty pages, mostly setting forth the exceptions to the mineral rights spoken to on the first page. Listed in the deed is the privately owned land within the boundaries described by that mineral rights deed that the Reynoldses did not get because the original land owners didn't sell the mineral rights.

I point this out because there is some confusion and ill feeling between people in this Toe River Valley who have owned land, or whose families have owned land, for 125 or so years or longer. Sometimes the current owners of these mineral rights say to a land owner that you can't do this or you can't do that because we own the mineral rights, and you, the land owner, do not.

I want to point out that there is one page describing the boundaries of those mineral rights and fifty or maybe more pages describing the land that is excepted from those mineral rights. One fourth of the people of Mitchell County do not know for which properties the mineral rights are held by the land owner and for which properties the mineral rights are held separately. I talked with a family in 1994 that was real upset because one of these mineral rights owners came to them and told them that they couldn't quarry or mine rocks on their farm, a farm that had been in their family for something like 125 years. I want anyone who reads this to know that most of the land in Mitchell County inside the boundaries described by the mineral rights deed is excepted from that deed.

My son and I own and look after approximately one thousand acres. None, absolutely none, of those acres is included in the mineral rights that the Reynoldses bought and that the ten or twelve men bought from the Reynoldses. Our land is clear. I wish that

A.D. Harrell grouse hunting; Mitchell County, North Carolina, 1966. Photo by Joel Arrington, North Carolina Division of Travel and Tourism. Note the steepness of the terrain in the background.

every citizen in this county knew what that deed says about their property rights.

I'll attempt to name a few families that have played a major part in the history and development of Mitchell County. These family names are Garland, Grindstaff, Philipson, Harrell, Hughes, Barnett, Miller, Masters, Bryant, Griffith, Bradshaw, and Byrd. Those families go back to the early development of Mitchell County. It is difficult to go back beyond 1870 to find records of the Mitchell County families from the Registrar of Deeds office because sometime in that period the records burned, making it difficult to find some detailed information.

CHAPTER FIVE

Family and Church Life

Childhood

My childhood family consisted of my dad, mother, one brother, Bruce, and five sisters: Helen, Mildred, Edna, Juanita, and Carol. My parents were honest and industrious, and they taught us to be likewise. I've heard my mother say time and time again that she had more sympathy for a thief than she had for a lazy person.

My parents lived on a farm and worked in agriculture entirely. My dad bragged time and time again that he never spent a day on a public works job in his life. By public works, he meant industry or something outside the farm. They lived on a farm that was their entire life and their entire income. As far back as I can remember, my dad was on daylight saving time, plus one hour. His day started at four o'clock and went until all priority work was done.

I recall the years back when a traveling group of men with a threshing machine went from one farm to another and threshed wheat, oats, rye, whatever the farm might have. That threshing went on throughout the community for about a month in August or early September after the grain was cut, shocked, and completely dry.

The threshing machine group came to my father and mother's place, to our place. They threshed one afternoon for an hour or two or three, then my parents fed them supper, got them bedded down for the night, and next morning got them up early and fed them breakfast. By early, I would say about four o'clock. While some of those threshers were stumbling around the house after breakfast, waiting for it to get daylight, I heard one of them say to another one, "It don't take long to stay all night at Luther Harrell's, does it?"

As to my mother's industriousness, I remember the time we had a snow something like three or four feet deep, so deep that nobody could do anything on the farm other than feed the pigs, feed the cattle, feed the chickens, and this 'n that. No outside field work could be done. My brother and I were sitting inside, beside the fire. We sat by the fire probably for two days, other than what time we were out doing the feeding.

My mother apparently got tired of us two fellows sitting beside the fire because she said, "I want you two to get out of here and go to work. Do something, just anything."

One of us commented that you can't do anything with this much snow on the ground.

She said, "How about getting two big shovels and shoveling the snow back and making some tobacco beds?" That was my mother's idea of being industrious. Snow or no snow, something should be done.

At a very early age, about four years old, all we children had jobs to do. We fed the hogs, we milked the cows, we went to the pasture and drove the cows in, we shucked corn, we hoed corn, we worked in the garden, we picked beans, we strung beans. There was something going on all the time—a real busy group of children.

Of course our mother cooked on a wood cookstove and that warmed up the kitchen. The rest of the house was warmed by an open fireplace. Dried wood was burned in the fireplace. During the day, that wood was kept on the fire with no problem; whoever came by when the fire was getting low put on some more wood.

A.D. Harrell's early family. Sitting, from left to right: Edna, father Luther, mother Arizona, Mildred, and Bruce. Standing, from left to right: Carol, Helen, A.D., and Juanita.

When night time came and everybody went to bed, that was another situation.

Every night, when everybody was ready to go to bed, the live embers in that fireplace, usually with one new stick of wood added to them, were completely covered up with ashes so that in the morning there would be some live coals in that fireplace with which to start a new fire. Once in a while in this valley in which we lived there would be one family (there were about five or six families that lived within a radius of half a mile of here) that would not cover up their embers good enough. Come morning, they wouldn't have any fire. I remember several times in which some neighbor, sometimes maybe even our own family, would go with some kind of metal container, a pot of some kind, to a neighbor's house and get enough live fire coals to carry back to build a fire with.

Remedies from an Earlier Time

I remember clearly, when I was about ten years old, that my sister Helen, who is two years older than I, got sick with a sore throat. I remember that my parents said she had the thrash. What the thrash was, I don't know, but she had a sore throat, and now I think she had what the doctors call strep throat. She was a sick girl. My parents went and asked Uncle Wylie Harrell, who was the oldest man in the community, to come over and "bleed" or "cup" Helen.

Here is what they did. They turned the little girl over on her stomach and on her bare back, about half way down the spine, they cut with a straight razor two tiny slits in the form of a cross, one right across the other, deep enough so each of them bled a little bit—not a great deal, but a little bit. Then, Uncle Wylie took a lighted match, held a drinking glass upright and dropped that match in that drinking glass. When that match had just about gone out (it had apparently burned up what oxygen was in the glass), he turned that glass upside down and put that glass over the cut spot on Helen's back. The vacuum formed by that match burning up the oxygen pulled the blood out of Helen's back. This process was called either cupping or bleeding.

I thought that was real unusual, but it must not have been so unusual at one time. Less than five years ago, I was reading a book on the U.S. presidents. When one president sometime in the early 1800s got sick, he was cupped or bled exactly in the way I have described here. Both my sister Helen and the president lived in spite of being bled or cupped.

One other medical practice in the field of ancient remedies or native remedies, or what have you, I would like to record here. It was the practice in some families, and apparently a belief, that when a child got real sick and they couldn't find a doctor or any other remedies to help the child get better, the remedy of last resort was for somebody to split a living black gum tree wide enough for that sick child to be passed through it.

Until four or five years ago, there stood on this ridge close to my house, a black gum tree that had been split by my grandfather, Kinsey Byrd, when his son Hal was sick as a child, somewhere around 1918 or that general time frame. Hal evidently got better; I don't think from the black gum split, but he lived to be an adult man. He spent his working years in the north somewhere and came back here in 1986. He worked here for a year or two, then was killed when a bulldozer turned over on him right near where they split that black gum tree.

Those remedies are something. Of course, black gum is hard to split, and how they split a black gum wide enough to pull a baby through, I don't know. I've heard the story time and time again and I've seen the tree. Marshall Street cut the tree down and made lumber out of it some four years ago.

We own some property at the head of Pate Creek that has a cemetery on it. According to the headstones, the last person buried there was buried over a hundred years ago. The cemetery stones indicate it was used by the Honeycutt family. It is real interesting to note that in that cemetery there are many little graves that are about eighteen inches long, some five or six in the same cemetery, indicating that those children of about one year in age died of diphtheria, or pneumonia, or strep throat, or something like that.

The Short End of the Stick

I have one brother, younger than I by seven years. His name is Bruce. I am the outdoors man. Bruce is the more studious type. He would rather read and watch television on a snowy day as to be out in the snow. He's probably got more sense than I have. Anyway, I enjoy being outdoors, out in the woods.

When I was in my teens and Bruce was probably nine, I said to him one morning, "Let's go rabbit hunting."

He asked, "How are we going to catch one? We don't have a dog. We don't have a gun. They can run faster than we can, and there's snow on the ground. I don't see how you're going to catch a rabbit."

"I'll tell you how we'll catch him. We'll track him up. And if he goes into a hollow tree, we'll put a stick up that hollow tree and twist the skin up and pull him out. And if he goes into a hole, we'll dig him out. But we'll get him."

So I talked Bruce into going against his better judgment.

We took off up a ridge line and I looked into a hollow log, a log that was about twenty feet long, laying on the ground. There sat a rabbit, in there out of the snow, out of the wind, his ears sticking up, his eyes just shining. He had it made.

"Okay, Bruce," I said. "I found one."

"What do you want me to do?"

"Come over here to the end of this log, the little end, and get down on your knees and hold your hands at the opening. When that rabbit runs out of there, you grab him and catch him and hold on to him."

"What's going to make him come out?"

"I'm going over here and cut me a pole long enough to reach that rabbit. When I punch it, he'll come out of there." So I went and cut me a pole.

When I came back to the end of the log I was going to punch from, I thought, "Well, I'd better go out there to Bruce and check to see if he is in the right position." So I walked around to the other end of the log. I got Bruce to hunker down just a little more to where he could see if the rabbit started to run and be ready to close some hands on him.

We got set up and everything looked perfect to me. There was no way that rabbit could get away.

I went back to my end of the log and put that stick in there and punched that rabbit and out he went. I raised up to see if Bruce had the rabbit. What I saw wasn't any rabbit. It was Bruce wiping the blood off of his face.

"What on earth has happened to you?" I said.

"That rabbit has killed me!"

The rabbit had run through Bruce's hands, into his face, and all four feet had gone to spinning right in his face to get away from him. Bruce had scratches from his hairline plumb down to his chin on both cheeks, and some on his nose. He was a bloody mess.

Bruce said, "A.D., if you ever get me out here again, I'm going to take that stick to you."

The Trip to Johnson City

One of my fondest childhood memories is of my father in the fall of the year driving a covered wagon with a team of mules to Johnson City, Tennessee. He had another man, a hired man who stayed at my Dad's, drive a second wagon and team of mules. Those trips to Johnson City were to sell farm produce—excess farm produce.

One lucky day, my parents agreed that I could go along. I was probably seven or eight or nine years old. We got in that wagon early in the morning and drove toward Johnson City. You cannot drive a team and a wagon from our house to Johnson City (it's about twenty-nine miles) in one day, so we would drive all day on

Monday and get within six or seven miles of Johnson City, then make camp.

In making camp, we would take the teams out of the wagons, water the mules, and turn them around in reverse order from the way they pulled the wagons to eat oats and corn from feed boxes set up in the front of the wagons. We'd let them stand there all night. In the morning, we'd feed and water them again and take them on down the road.

We would sleep in the wagon, underneath the Conestoga cover. The next morning, that would be Tuesday, we would go on into town. On Tuesday, Wednesday, and Thursday, my dad and the hired man would sell the produce from those two wagons. On Friday morning, we'd head back. Sometime late Friday night we'd get home.

On that trip we took our own food and did our own cooking, or the adults did. What we did was take a box—called the "rations" box—that was two-and-a-half feet long by two feet wide with a depth of about fourteen or fifteen inches, and put in silverware, knives, forks, and spoons; metal plates similar to pie pans; metal drinking cups; dish towels, and so forth. We also put in a good helping of bacon, which would be side meat from hogs that we had raised ourselves. We also put in a slice of country ham, sugar, salt, coffee, pepper, onions, and potatoes. Those were the basic food items that went in that rations box.

Along with that box we had a gallon bucket to make coffee in. It was usually an emptied Karo syrup bucket that had been cleaned up and had two holes punched in the top of it. A wire with a long, wide curve on it was run through those two holes, so a man could hold the bucket above a fire without getting burned.

Coffee making consisted of filling that bucket about four-fifth's full of cold water and putting the necessary amount of coffee in it to make some fairly strong coffee and setting that bucket on the fire and letting it come to a boil. As coffee out in the open like that is boiling, the grounds will come to the top and they will tend to collect on the top. After that water has boiled awhile, the grounds will settle to the bottom and leave the top in the cooling process. That doesn't mean the coffee will be cool enough to drink. It will still blister your tongue. But the grounds do settle back to the bottom and get out of the way. When that coffee boils in that manner, made out in the open air, it is real fine coffee, and the aroma from it is something out of this world.

Food was cooked over an open camp fire. We took a little dry wood from home, as I recall, to start that fire. To fix the standard meal for the crew, we peeled and sliced some potatoes and put those potatoes in a large frying pan, one about twelve or fourteen inches across. We poured enough water on those potatoes until we could barely see the water coming up through the potatoes. Then we took some bacon grease, about half a teacup full, and poured it on top of those potatoes. Then we sliced two or three pieces of bacon and put that on top and took two big onions and sliced them up and put that on top of the potatoes, water, bacon, and all. We put that on the campfire and put some type of lid on it, and cooked it till done. Of course, we salted and peppered it to people's satisfaction.

That is a real fine meal to cook out of doors. That is the meal that we cooked, I believe, every single night on that trip. Still to this day, once in a while, in our own kitchen here I will fix that set up on the cook stove. It is never as good fixed on a cook stove on the inside as it is fixed on a campfire on the outside, but it is a fine dish. It is one of my throwbacks from seventy years ago and still a good dish.

On those Conestoga wagon trips, our cooking for breakfast consisted of country cured ham, ham that we cured on the farm, plus eggs, coffee, and loaf bread. We bought our bread (ten cents a loaf) for all our meals, for the evening meal and lunch as well as for breakfast. But it was real fine eating; it was real fine food. It was the same thing, potatoes and onions and so forth at the evening meal, and country ham and eggs and coffee for breakfast. I don't remember any fruit or any vegetables or any milk. Of course, you may know that any food cooked outside over an open fire has a little better flavor than any food cooked inside.

Once in a while on this trip we would go to a local cafe for one meal. It is interesting to note that you could get a full meal at that time for thirty-five cents: a full meal with a drink and a dessert for thirty-five cents. We didn't go to those cafes often, but once in a while we did.

We camped and cooked in Johnson City on a vacant lot or a vacant square. My memory says it was at South Roan Street and Walnut. Sometimes there would be four or five other wagons there with people camping and cooking. Frequently, we would have visitors from town during our evening meal. They would come to watch us cook and to enjoy the aroma from the food and to talk with us and to visit with us.

We made several friends from that evening cooking. Some of those friendships continue down to this day. I have friends that I made seventy years ago that I still see once in a while.

That trip is something that I wish all my children and grandchildren and great-grandchildren could experience. That's just something from another age that I'd like for them to know about.

Early Education

As for school, we children in this family went to school at Harrell Hill, up where our community house at the Pleasant Grove Brethren Church is at the present time. A two-room school house was there then, with two teachers. The building was heated with two wood stoves. In front of the school room was an iron stove. It fitted in some way with the teacher's desk and the seats and what have you. We kept warm by keeping that stove hot with dried wood from a stack in one corner of the school room. I don't remember anything about who furnished the wood, how it got there, or where it came from.

We had a water bucket with a dipper. Two children, the lucky ones, would be sent sometime during the day to the nearest house for a bucket of water. That was always a chore that would get us out of the school house, something that I particularly liked to do.

We went to that school for first, second, third, fourth, and fifth grade. After fifth grade, we switched to Tipton Hill, where we would go to sixth and seventh grade and to high school.

Transportation to Tipton Hill was interesting. We walked from my house on down the creek to the first bridge that crosses Rock Creek. There, we got in a Conestoga wagon pulled by a team of horses. The wagon hauled us to school and hauled us back again. I had no idea what the driver of the wagon and team did from the time he let us out at the school house until he picked us up to take us back. The man I recalled driving that wagon was a gentleman named Grady Masters. We walked down the creek to get the wagon for a few years, then finally the wagon came up the creek farther to pick us up where the road forks to go to Ray Bryant's. I remember waiting there, at that fork in the road, for that wagon.

I don't remember what grade I was in, probably eighth or ninth, when that wagon was switched to a bus. During my high school years we walked from where we lived, across the hill by the church, and down to the fork in the road that goes to Ray Bryant's to catch the school bus. At no time during my high school years did the bus come by on this road to pick us up by our house. I'm sure that bus did start coming by our house before my youngest sister graduated from high school, but not while I was going to high school.

Edna Goes to College

I have mentioned that there were seven children in our family. One of my mother's life-long determinations was that those seven children would go through college. I don't think she had any plan in mind about how to pay for it, but she was determined that those seven children would go to college.

My sister Helen was the first one to start college. I was the second, and Mildred was in college at the same time I was. Then along came the next girl, Edna, who had decided that she was not going to college. But Mother had decided that all seven of us were going to college.

About three days before time for Edna to leave for college, Mother went upstairs to pack a trunk of clothes for her. At night Edna unpacked that trunk and hung up those clothes in the closet. The next day Mother went upstairs and found those clothes hanging up, so she packed the trunk a second time.

She called the young lady in and said, "Edna, I've packed that trunk again. That's the second time I've packed it. Understand that you are going to school. If I find that trunk unpacked again in the morning, there's that peach tree right down beside the creek, and I'll send you down to that peach tree to get a limb, not a little limb, but one maybe two feet long. You'll bring it up here to me, and if you unpack that trunk, I'll wear that limb out over your hind end. Now do you understand that? You're going to school!"

My mother was not being hard on Edna; she was doing the best thing she could for that girl. Although it was hard to do, she was doing what should have been done. Mother was determined that all seven of us would go to school. All seven of us did earn a college degree, the gift of the determination and the will power and the love that a hardworking mother had for her children.

Edna went on to school, took four years, and graduated. I've heard her say time and time again, "If I'd done what I wanted to instead of what Mother wanted me to, I would have been absolutely ruined. I would never have amounted to a thing."

The Fly, a Courtship Story

After I finished college and got my degree and teaching certificate, I taught two years and then the following summer I went back to Appalachian State University and did some post graduate work and thereby upgraded my teaching certificate. By doing that I upgraded my salary a little bit. In those days, the salary needed to be upgraded; the first month I taught with a grade A certificate and college degree I got a check for eighty-six dollars and thirty-seven cents. I believe that check went up six dollars a month with experience, which finally got me up to ninety dollars the second year. Be that as it may, I went back to school the summer after I taught two years to upgrade my certificate.

In that summer school I met a young lady from Hoke County, North Carolina, from the little town of Raeford. She was in summer school doing the very same thing that I was doing. Her name was Mary Alma. Well I dated Mary Alma some during that summer and came to appreciate the girl and we got along right well. When fall came, I went back home to work and she went back to Raeford in Hoke County to work. Sometime later that fall, I drove to Raeford to visit Mary Alma.

Now to drive from my house to Raeford takes about four hours, so it wasn't the process of seeing a young lady, visiting with her, having a date with her and then coming back home and going to bed; it was a process of driving that far and visiting the girl and finding some place to stay.

Well, I drove down to Raeford. Before Mary Alma and I went out for the evening, her dad and mother came to me and said since it was ten or so miles to the nearest motel and since they had extra bedrooms, they would be glad to have me if I'd like to spend the night there. That would keep me from having to drive somewhere else to find a motel.

I accepted the invitation and slept that night at Mary Alma's home. The next morning when they woke me up to go to break-fast, the table was already set, with place settings for Mary Alma, and her dad and her mother, and me and, I believe, for one other person, a sister maybe. In that table setting, each cereal bowl had a serving of cornflakes. On the table was milk and sugar to put on those corn flakes, so it was clear that the first thing we were going to eat was a bowl of cereal, cornflakes.

We started eating and talking and visiting back and forth and carrying on a conversation. I poured sugar on my cornflakes and poured milk on them and stirred them up a little bit. When I stirred those cornflakes, a fly—a housefly—crawled up out of my cornflakes to where I could see it, but nobody else could.

I thought, "If Mary Alma and her mother see this, they will be absolutely embarrassed to death, so I must not let them know that there's a fly in my cereal."

I took my spoon, and I dug me a hole, all the time trying to carry on a conversation. I dug me a hole inside that bowl and I rolled that fly in it and I covered him up. I moved my spoon to the other side of the cereal bowl and I started eating.

I ate three or four bites, and we talked a little. I kept my eyes squared on the other side of that bowl to see what was going on.

That fine fly crawled up out of that cereal the second time. I was getting concerned. I dug me another hole and put him down in it and covered him up and that time I tromped on him a little with my spoon.

I thought, "Well, I'll end that. I'll just eat off the top of him and hopefully kill him, so he'll stay down there and they won't know."

While that was going on, I recalled hearing that one time Abraham Lincoln was invited out to some friend's house there in Washington and he found a fly in his food. Great man that he was, rather than embarrass his host, he ate that dern fly. If Abraham Lincoln could eat a fly, then maybe A.D. Harrell could eat a fly, too. But I wanted to try one more time to get by without *that*.

I ate a little more cornflakes and talked a little more and decided what I would do if I had to. While I was talking and thinking, that blessed fly crawled up again. I learned then that when a fly crawls up out of milk his eyes look kind of red, and I also learned that you can't drown a fly. You can put it under the water, you can put it under the milk and this 'n that, but it just won't drown. You can't drown a fly. I thought that third time he came up that I'd just put me a little cereal right on top of him, I'd take me one big bite, and I'd eat that S-O-B. So I did.

I ate that fine fly. I was real conscious for the next hour or two to see if I had any ill after effects, but I didn't have. Of course the family never knew that fly was in my cereal.

But once in a while to this day, Geneva and I can get in an argument about something. If I get real ornery (and I do frequently get hard to get along with), every once in a while Geneva will say, "It must be that fly. It must be that fly he ate fifty years ago, a delayed reaction to that fly, because nobody could be that ornery."

We get a lot of mileage out of that fly.

One other subnote to that deal. In school sometimes when the class got real dull and the students got to just wishing that blessed period would be over, I'd tell them that fly story. It never failed; it woke them up every single time.

Tribute to Geneva

On February 4, 1990, a Sunday, I delivered the following talk in our church:

> For the past few months, our minister has asked us to take turns during the service to acknowledge some one in the community who has been a positive influence in the church and has been a positive influence in our lives. Giving tribute to our forefathers is well and good, and we should honor those who gave us our heritage; we owe them a lot. But there is nothing wrong in honoring those who are still alive, while they are present to hear our praise. Today, I plan to honor one who is here in this church, and who will, hopefully, appreciate what I have to say.
>
> You will recall that last Sunday our minister gave an account of a person in the Old Testament searching for a bride. That's the story of Rebekah; it has to do with some Biblical character searching for a bride. He went off in the countryside looking, and he met a young lady at a well, drawing up water from the well. He said to himself, if she just waters my camels, I'll go on looking somewhere else. But if she waters my camels and then turns and gives some water to me, I'll give that lady a little further checking out and so forth. That's the story of Rebekah at the well.
>
> Now to my story. Back in my high school days I made some decisions about the kind of girl I wanted to marry. One thing that influenced my thinking is that when I was in elementary school,

probably in fourth or fifth grade, it came to my knowledge that there were several families in the general area with retarded children, some of them physically retarded, some of them mentally retarded, some of them both physically and mentally retarded. And in some families was more than one such child. At an early age I asked my parents about that. They told me it was due to people marrying who were closely related to each other, like first cousins marrying first cousins, or second cousins marrying, and so forth.

In these mountain valleys and in this general area there was not a large pool from which to select a mate. That gene pool was made up of four or five or possibly six families, and over the years those families had intermarried and the results had not been good. With that knowledge in the back of my mind, I decided that I would never marry any girl from Mitchell County. She would have to be from another county, and, hopefully, maybe from another state, because I didn't like what I had seen with children who were having some difficulties, and I thought I knew the answer to it.

I wanted the girl that I was eventually going to marry to be a member of the Brethren church. (At one time, talking when I was about four or five years old, I didn't know there was anything but Brethren churches. I might not have known there were Baptist churches and Methodist churches.) Of course, being male, I wanted that young lady to be attractive. I mentioned that I wanted to get some genes for our children that would add some strength to the Harrell family, to the Harrell generation, I felt like we needed some.

I wanted that girl to be from a farm or agricultural background because I had grown up with an agricultural background. I loved outdoor life, I loved agriculture, and I loved animals, and I wanted a girl who could understand that love.

I wanted her to understand how a man could get up at three a.m. and walk miles to be at a deer stand by daylight. I wanted her to understand that when I broke the ice on the South Toe River and waded across to retrieve a grouse that that was completely normal; I wasn't really off. It was just the grouse hunter's desire to get across that river and through that ice to pick up that grouse he had shot. I wanted a girl that would understand the thrill of walking over a green meadow and appreciate the smell of new mown hay.

With that in the background, I had some idea of who I was looking for.

Fifty years ago the Brethren church had a real active youth organization in the Southeastern District. Summer meetings that would last several days were held at various locations. At one such meeting, held at New Haven Church in Allegheny County, North Carolina, I saw the most attractive girl I had ever seen. She was simply beautiful. But there was a fly in the ointment; she had a boyfriend with her and I had taken a girl from here with me. However, I did get her name and address. Her address was Campobello, South Carolina.

Later on, I went to visit her and I found out several things about her. Her family was active in the Mill Creek Brethren Church, now probably the largest church in the Southeastern District. Her father was church treasurer and he had been church treasurer for years. As a matter of history, he served as church treasurer until he died. I learned that she had graduated as valedictorian of her class. I learned that her family owned and operated a farm that produced cotton. Most important of all, I learned that she lived the principals of Christian religion as taught by George Branscom, Reuel Pritchett, John Reed, and Joe Henderson, all great Brethren church leaders of fifty years ago.

Well I married that girl. We have four fine children and they're all university graduates. Those new genes did the job. Those genes are very important. A plaque on our mantel reads, "All hearts grow warmer in the presence of one who gives freely for the love of giving. A love that deepens and grows as a blooming rose." This plaque was presented to Geneva by her four children.

One evening at the supper table after we had been married forty-nine years, just Geneva and I alone, the children all away, we were sitting across the table from each other, having the evening meal, I looked over at Geneva and smiled and said, "Geneva, I'm real glad I married you. I don't think I'd have been as happy with anyone else, so I'm real glad that you're the girl I married."

Geneva looked up, smiled. Those pretty brown eyes twinkled. This is what she said, "A.D., there have been days when I wished that I had married anybody else on the face of this earth." (When I made that comment in church, all of the good brothers and good sisters stood up in a fun-filled exclamation point.)

We, Geneva and I and the entire family, acknowledge with gratitude our debt to the Church of the Brethren. For what the church has given us, we are thankful.

Geneva, I want you to stand up and take a bow, for you are truly a modern Rebekah, and I love you.

Philosophy of Raising Children

My wife, Geneva, and I have held fast to a particular philosophy in raising our own four fine children, Douglas, Judy, Larry, and Rose Marie. We base this philosophy on what we learned from our parents and the communities where we grew up.

We believe that there are two or three things that parents can do for their children that will stand them in good stead as long as they live. One of these things is to teach them the value of work. We feel it is important for children to learn to work, to learn to enjoy working. This whole economy, this whole society, and our whole business world is tuned to work, so from early on we have emphasized the value of work and responsibility.

We believe that it is real important to learn to do a job well. We believe that the satisfaction received from a job well done will stay with you as long as you live. We think if it's done well enough, it will bring a feeling of pleasure every time you think of it, and that is real important. We believe that the value and pleasure received from doing a job well is far greater than winning any athletic contest and will last far longer. We have attempted to instill in our children a desire to work, an enjoyment of work, and pride in doing a job well.

The second thing we feel children should have is a basic foundation in religion, and for us that is the Christian religion and the Brethren church, the church we were brought up in. We feel that to give them a basic foundation in the Christian religion is to give them a compass, a guiding light. That basic Christian religion will serve as a north star, something to guide them. Without that compass, we feel there will be times when they are floundering about, without any compass or direction.

Third, we want to give them all the education that their minds can absorb. In thinking about paying for that education for those children, early on it was clear to us, the birthdays of our children

being what they were, that we would have two of them in the university system at the same time for three years in a row and that
we probably would have three in the university system for one
year. Knowing how expensive college educations are, we knew
that we had to get to work and put some finances together to pay
for those things.

With that in mind, we decided that I would continue teaching in
the high school and that in addition we would set up a grade A
dairy operation and get involved in normal agricultural activities
on the land that we happened to own. Of course, we'd have to
farm with hired labor, with supervision. But for some several years,
all of the years that I taught, we operated a grade A dairy farm,
milking some fifty-six registered Guernsey cows.

We were able to put together a financial package that did pay for
the education of those four children. We made it clear to them
early on that as long as they wanted to go to school, as long as they
were making good grades and satisfactory progress, that we would
pay the expenses.

Each of them worked while they were in college. Each of them
found a job and each of them contributed greatly to the expenses.
With what they contributed and what we could pay, they all took
university degrees. Rose Marie even took a Ph.D. degree.

Pleasant Grove Church of the Brethren

I want to comment on this Brethren church, known as the Pleasant Grove Church, that sits on top of Harrell Hill. That is the
church of my family, mine and Geneva's, our present family, and
the church of the Harrell family of our ancestry. The first memories
that I have of that church go back to 1921. In the '20s, that church

From left to right: Rose Marie, Doug, Judy, A.D., Geneva, and Larry.

was a small wooden frame building, painted white. It had a bell, I recall.

Sunday school started at ten o'clock. The first class I recall was what we called the Card Class. It had the youngest children in the church, anywhere, I reckon, from babies in arms up to four or five years old. I still recall that the Card Class took up about two benches in that church, which meant it had somewhere between fourteen and eighteen children in it.

An important part of that Card Class was a little picture card that the teacher would give out to each child on Sunday. That card was two and one half by two inches in size. On one side of each card was a picture of some religious setting or theme or so forth. Underneath that picture was a memory verse, a short verse from the Bible. Every child in that Card Class was expected to memorize that verse. I don't recall what was on the back of the cards, probably something on the general subject of the lesson. The first teacher that I recall from that Card Class was Hattie Masters, Mrs. Grady Masters.

A thing that is real distinct in my memory, even as far back as 1924 and '25, is the fact that in that Card Class we tried every Sunday to have a penny to put in the collection plate. It was a real unhappy child in that Card Class if he didn't have a penny to put in the collection plate. That same thing is true of our young people today. They want something for themselves, something in their little hands, to drop in that collection plate when it comes around. When I was a child, and my brother and sisters were children, all we ever hoped to have was one penny. I think we probably had a penny for each Sunday's collection.

The Brethren church was a real important part of my childhood. Not only did we have two benches filled with Card Class children, we also had a church filled with adults. The church was the site of all the social activity on Sunday and frequently on Wednesday nights, when we'd have what was called prayer meeting. Youth groups would have box suppers in which a girl would pack some box with a favorite cake or something, take it to a set up where an auctioneer would auction these boxes off. It was expected that her boyfriend would bid that box off, regardless of what the price was. We all knew what boyfriend belonged to what girl, so when her box came up to be auctioned off, the other fellows ran it up just as high as they could, knowing all the time that the boyfriend would have to bid that box off. The other fellows got a big kick out of seeing how high they could run that box up, making the poor boy pay dearly for it.

Over the years, the congregation tended to get smaller, particularly down through the '60s and '70s. In the '70s it got so it looked like the church might close the doors.

In the '80s we experienced a decided growth. Growth hinged round the fact that we had three young families with children move back to this community. One of the families was Keith Masters, his wife, Carol, and their children. Another family was John Smith, his wife, Barbara, and their children, and there was our son Doug, his wife, Barbara, and their children. About the time these families moved back, our church gradually turned over the reins of control from the older group to these younger men. It is heartening and pleasing to see how much movement these young men got going, how many things they did. They straightened up the community house. They pushed the building of the basement in the church. They hired new pastors. This group of young men just simply changed gears; they went into a faster gear and got things done. Our community is much, much better for them, particularly in the affairs of our church and the community club.

We are still a small church, only forty-five or fifty members, but over the years, our members have been important in the development of Mitchell County. In that small church we count fifteen university graduates and two Ph.D.'s. From our church over the last fifteen or so years have come the following: a principal of the Tipton Hill Primary and Middle School; a chairman of the Mayland Community College Board; a chairman of the Mitchell County Board of Commissioners; two members (one of whom was chairman) of the Mitchell County Board of Education; the national sales supervisor for a major business enterprise headquartered in Wichita, Kansas; the head of the Federal Head Start program for Mitchell, Avery, and Yancey counties; the head of the Farmers Home Administration program for Mitchell, Avery, and Yancey counties; the first female agency manager for the North Carolina Farm Bureau Federation, an insurance company; the Mitchell County building inspector; a member of the Bakersville Medical Clinic Board; a member of the Mitchell County Public Library Board; a member of the Mitchell County Soil and Water Conservation District Board; a supervisor in the North Carolina Department of Natural Resources unit office in Asheville; an official with the Customs Division of the U.S. Treasury Department; and the dean of continuing education at Sumter Technical College in Sumter, South Carolina. I know I'm bragging, but hopefully at my age I can get by with it.

Now I'm through a bit of the history of the Brethren Church that sits on Harrell Hill and I come down to the present day, July the ninth, 1994. On July the eighth, I went to the conference of the Southeastern District of the Brethren Church, which was held at Black Mountain. I think a resume of this district conference would be a good way to end this segment on the Brethren Church.

We had a service at this district conference in the Blue Ridge assembly room at Black Mountain. There were five or six hundred people in that assembly, and we had as a speaker a gentleman who pastors a church in Johnson City, Tennessee. Before he started his sermon, he asked if there were any people in the audience who would like to stand up and comment briefly on any blessings they had received from being members of the Brethren Church. After a few speakers had gone, I stood and indicated that I would like to make a few remarks.

I looked over the audience and said, "It is clear in looking over this audience that I may well be the oldest man in this house. I don't feel like the oldest man in this house, but I may look like the oldest man in this house. I want to take this opportunity to express my appreciation for the Brethren Church and what it has meant to me individually and to my family down through the years. I have come to these district conferences six or seven or possibly eight times in my life, spanning a period of about sixty years. I'm older than sixty years. Knowing the people of these conferences and knowing you people here tonight has been a tremendous blessing to me. I realize now, as do you, that this may well be the last conference I am ever able to come to. Should that be the case, I want it

Pleasant Grove Church of the Brethren.

on record that the Brethren Church and these district conferences have meant a tremendous amount to A.D. Harrell and to his entire family. If this should be the last district conference that I am able to attend, I want to tell all of you that you are fine people. I love you. I've enjoyed fellowship with you, and I want to say God bless you all. Thank you."

Brethren Ministers

The first preacher I remember hearing in that church on top of Harrell Hill was the Reverend J.R. Jackson. I heard Reverend Jackson about 1925 or '26. Down through the years, I continued to hear Reverend Jackson once in a while. He preached some in our church here. He also preached some in churches in Texas, in Virginia, in Pennsylvania, in Tennessee. It seemed like every twenty or twenty-five years he would drift back to our area and preach somewhere. I remember Reverend Jackson with a real fond, loving memory.

Some fifteen years ago he preached for the last time in our little brick church that stands on the hill now. At that time his faculties were beginning to fail, but here was a man who had spent his entire life preaching to Brethren people. He was not an educated man from the standpoint of the number of schools he had graduated from, but he was a dedicated fellow. He didn't use perfect language, but his dedication made up for any mistakes he might possibly have made in English.

As the man grew older, Geneva and I started to send him a check at Christmas time. I felt that money was well deserved because he had spent a lifetime preaching. I know that he was paid very little. He had come down to the last years of his life with no retirement fund from his ministry, but just living from the goodness of the people around him, so we sent him a donation.

The first year he sent us a real kind, gracious thank you note in a real clear, legible hand. The next year we sent him another donation. Come January the second time, another thank you note came but the hand writing was not quite as clear. The third year rolled around and we sent him a third donation and he wrote back again. That time it was difficult to read the handwriting.

We sent him the fourth one and that time we received a thank you note that was typed on a piece of business paper. It was clear that he had typed it out using a hunt and peck system; he hadn't found, in some cases, the proper capital letters. He hadn't hit some of the proper keys, but he did manage in his hunt and peck system to get across to us that he thanked us for our kind donation. We sent the fifth donation, but the gentleman died before we got the fifth thank you note. I don't know when the two of us have received as much satisfaction from any little gift we have given as we did from the donations to Preacher Jackson. We still have those thank you notes in our files.

The next preacher in that Brethren Church to have much influence on me was a preacher named Fred Dancey. He was pastor of our church here on Harrell Hill when he was in his early twenties. He and his wife came here about 1930 and he served as our pastor for some few years. Fred was a fine speaker. He was a handsome young man. He had a lot of humor about him, a lot of wit. He had a big smile for everybody. He did a lot of laughing, a lot of talking. He could slap people on the back and make them feel comfortable and make them feel good. I think Fred took to heart the passage in the Bible that says, "Rejoice and be exceeding glad for great is your reward in heaven."

Fred didn't get involved in much fire and brimstone and pounding on the podium and so forth. He could get his message across with a fine public relations pitch. Something real important here, the young people of our church loved that Fred Dancey and they loved his wife.

Fred Dancey came back to our church from time to time, after he left it as the regular pastor. He would hold revivals or hold a Sunday service or come back for a funeral. Over a period of some twenty years, up until he got to where he was physically unable to come, Fred Dancey was the choice of most families to handle the funeral of a family member. He came here last in 1990, I believe, to help conduct a funeral, but Fred was about done carrying out the work of a ministry or doing the service of a funeral.

Fred and his wife, Frances, are in their nineties now, and living in North Wilkesboro, North Carolina. We are doing for Fred Dancey and Frances what we did for Preacher Jackson as long as he lived. We are sending a donation each Christmas. I don't know if they look forward to our donation or not; that's not important. I do know how much Geneva and I look forward to the thank you note that comes each January from Fred and Frances Dancey.

Some two years ago, on their sixtieth or seventieth wedding anniversary, Geneva and I drove from here to North Wilkesboro one Sunday. We went to their home, where Fred's children and the community people were having an open house. I don't know when we have enjoyed going to a friend's party more than going to Fred's and his wife's party. I know that we have never been received at anything we went to with any more open arms than Fred Dancey and his wife received us at that time.

I talk with Fred Dancey and Frances once in a while on the telephone now. I want to get on record how much he has meant to the Brethren Church here on Harrell Hill, how much he has meant to the Harrell family, and how much he has meant especially to Geneva and me and to our family.

In addition to Reverend Jackson and Fred Dancey, two other preachers had an important influence on my family and me. One of them was a gentleman named Reuel Pritchett, from the state of Tennessee. I remember him particularly for having flaming red hair and a red beard. For some reason I can't explain, I've never in the back of my mind associated people with red hair and red beards with preaching. I tend to associate such people with the other end of the spectrum. And I'd better not go into further detail on that. Reuel Pritchett was a terrific preacher and he did have red hair and a red beard. He preached in our church in about 1940.

Another preacher who had some influence on both Geneva and me was from Polk County, North Carolina, where Geneva was from originally. His name was George Branscom. He lived in Melvin Hills in Polk County and was the pillar of the Melvin Hills Brethren Church, a church that is still quite active.

Bruce and A.D. Sing in Church

It has been written that all men are created equal. That is not necessarily true. Quite clearly, some men are more equal than others. For example, most human beings have some musical ability. Some human beings have great musical ability. Some have mediocre musical ability. Some have minimal ability. But some human beings have no musical ability. In the latter category are my brother and I.

We learned before we were ten years old that we couldn't sing, that we couldn't carry a tune. That kind of concerned us. We were regularly going to church, and church people do a lot of singing. We tried and we tried, but we just couldn't sing.

We talked about the fact that other people could sing but we couldn't. I remember I was maybe twelve or thirteen, and Bruce was seven years younger.

One Sunday morning we were walking from our home, up the gravel road to our church. On our way, we were talking about our inability to sing. We decided that possibly we could sing, but we just didn't know it. We agreed that when we got to church that morning and they started to sing, we would open our mouths and sing just as loud as we could sing.

We went in and sat down, either on the back pew or on the next to the back pew in the church. When the minister announced the song number, we got us a song book and turned to that number. The song leader stood up and started the singing.

We lived up to our agreement. We opened our mouths and sung just as loud as we could sing. When we did that, all the good brothers and all the good sisters turned their heads around as if they were on swivels. (I wonder to this day why they didn't get cricks in their necks.) They turned their heads around to see what the commotion was, what all that squealing and so forth was going on in the back of the church. It was simply Bruce and I proving to the world that we couldn't sing.

Walter West's Baptism

Highway 226 runs north from Bakersville, North Carolina, by Buladean to the Tennessee state line at the Iron Mountain Gap. At the Tennessee state line this road becomes Tennessee highway 107 to Unicoi. In the 1920s, '30s, and '40s, this road wasn't paved. It wasn't graveled. It was a dirt road, muddy in wet weather and dusty in dry weather. This was the road my father traveled with a team and Conestoga wagon on the trips to Johnson City.

When you go down this road on the Tennessee side of the Iron Mountain, the first house is on the left side of the road, near the base of the mountain. In the 1920s, in this house lived a family by the name of West. My memory says the parents were Will and Mary West. I remember there were two boys, one named Burnie, about twenty years old, and one named Walter, about sixteen. This family was able to keep body and soul together by growing garden crops of corn, beans, potatoes, and various other vegetables. Some added income came from working in the timber industry, the logging and lumber industry, by cutting down trees with a misery whip.

A misery whip is a two-man cross-cut saw, with a handle on each end. Each man took an end, and they alternately pulled the saw back and forth against the grain of a tree until the tree was cut down. "Misery" is a pretty apt adjective to describe that saw.

This family's life was extremely hard, so they supplemented their income by making moonshine whiskey. They made two kinds of whiskey: clear, or white lightning, out of corn meal and red out of fermented rye. It was said that their whiskey was of an excellent quality.

Even today, seventy years later, I salute that family for their industriousness and for their effort. No welfare clients here.

As my father made several trips on this road, he came to know this family. I don't know if the original acquaintance was possibly to stop and buy some of their whiskey or possibly to stop and warm from getting cold on the trip across the mountain. But be that as it may, my father got to be a friend of the family.

This acquaintance resulted in my father's inviting the younger son to come and live at our house and work with him and pretty much live the life of an adopted son. Walter came and stayed at my father's house, probably for fifteen or so years. Those were the years that I would have been in what is now middle school.

I mentioned some of the things that the West family did to make a living, to have enough food for the table and so forth. In all the stories I heard about the West family, in all the things I knew about them, I never knew of any particular interest that they took in church affairs. In fact I'm not sure they ever went to church. It would tend to be my opinion that they did not attend church, although they were fine, honest, upright people, whiskey making nevertheless.

After Walter West had lived with my family some ten years, they got him to go to the Brethren church up here on Harrell Hill, not every Sunday, but some Sundays. Eventually through going to church and listening to the services and from the pressure of the local people (the local ministers and my dad and mother and people in the community) Walter West was finally encouraged to become a member of that church.

To become a member of the Brethren church, you go to the front of the church and indicate your intention to want to become a member. Next, a date is set up by the candidate and the church elders and so forth for a time to take that candidate to a nearby stream and baptize him. In our Brethren church (I say this with all due respect and humbleness and so forth to the people involved) the candidate was taken to a local stream and put under. His head and shoulders were completely submerged in the water three times by a local minister, or frequently by two ministers, one on either side of the candidate.

In this case, there were two ministers with Walter West. One of them was the Reverend Syd Bryant, who went into the water on Mr. West's left side. The other minister was the Reverend Vance Tipton. He went into the water on Mr. West's right side. Now we have three men in the water, waist deep.

When they go in the water, the man on the candidate's left side holds the candidate's left arm and puts his right hand on the head of the candidate. The minister on the right side of the candidate puts his left hand on the candidate's head, on top of the other minister's hand, and holds the candidate's right arm with his right hand. When they are ready, the ministers say, "I baptize you in the name of the Father," and they put the candidate's head under the water, face down. He comes up, they give him time to breathe and shake his head and get the water out of his ears and nose and so forth. Then, they put his head under a second time, saying, "I baptize you in the name of the Son." After they put him under a third time, saying, "I baptize you in the name of the Holy Ghost," they lead him up out of the water.

This particular baptism, which was performed some quarter of a mile below our house, was performed in the winter time. It wasn't mid-winter. It was either early winter or late winter, one. It wasn't cold enough to freeze ice, but it was cold weather.

Everything didn't go completely according to Hoyle. The good reverends put Walter West's head under the water the first time and the second time. Before they got ready to put his head under the third time, Mr. West got real cold. He broke loose, came out of the water, and ran. He left the stream and ran up the road to my father's house, wet and cold and not quite freezing to death, but I guess pretty close to it. He went upstairs and changed clothes and came back down and announced to all who were present at the time that that was all the religion that he could stand.

Walter later married a local Mitchell County girl, Miss M. Wilcox, daughter of the late Sam Wilcox. After the marriage, Walter returned to Tennessee. He worked in a machine shop on Walnut Street in Johnson City until he reached retirement age.

One day in 1985 a fine automobile came into our driveway. A beautiful young lady accompanied by an elderly man came up the walkway to our house. The man had a decided stoop of the shoulders, and he walked with some difficulty. I met them at the steps, took one look at the old man, then opened up my arms and embraced him. Walter West and his daughter had come to visit us.

"Miss Bonnie" Plays the Piano

At our Brethren church here at Harrell Hill, we have been fortunate in that we have had the same piano player for the church services for some thirty to forty years. That pianist, Miss Bonnie, is a fine piano player and a fine lady, and she has been faithful down through the years to playing at whatever service she was needed. Whether it be a Sunday service or a funeral or a wedding or whatever, she was always there, ready to do her part.

Walter West and his family lived in a cabin similar to this one.

There was twenty years ago a striking resemblance between Miss Bonnie and my wife, Geneva, especially when they were seated in the church, and you were looking at them from the back. There was quite a similarity in that they both had black hair and wore it shoulder length. It was not difficult to mistake them.

One Sunday morning, my wife and I went into the church, walked halfway down the aisle and sat down on the left side, before the service started. When the Sunday school superintendent got the service underway, he called Miss Bonnie to come up and play the piano.

Miss Bonnie wasn't there that day. The superintendent asked if there was someone else present who could play the piano.

My wife plays but she has been so busy all of her life that she hasn't practiced enough to be a real good pianist. But being the good soul that she is, she volunteered to substitute for Miss Bonnie. Geneva left the seat and went up to the piano and started playing. My memory says that she was playing "Shall We Gather at the River."

We were standing up to sing, and about the time Geneva had played one verse, a gentleman by the name of Elbert Bryant came into the pew where she had been, which means he was beside me, on my right side. Elbert Bryant had several interests in life. One of his primary interests was his love of singing. If there was a singing session going on in the general area and Mr. Bryant knew about it, he would go to that singing. He loved to sing. He could read the notes, he could sing the shaped notes, he could sing those do-re-mi-fa-sol notes, and he really enjoyed his singing. He was forever trying to set up a practice, or a singing session, at our church.

He picked up a songbook. We sang another verse and at the end of that verse, Geneva hit a sour note. Elbert Bryant punched me in the side a little bit and said, "Bonnie missed that one."

I said, "Yes, she did."

Well, we went on and sang a little more, and Geneva missed another note.

Elbert said, "Bonnie missed that one, too."

"Yes. She's missed a lot of 'em, hasn't she?"

"It gets worse all the time."

We sang another verse or so, and there was another sour note. Mr. Bryant allowed as how he was going to have trouble singing if Bonnie was going to miss so many notes in the piano playing.

"We might ought to try to do something about that," I said.

We sang another verse and had another mistake.

Mr. Bryant said, "That's just about the worst I've ever heard. What do you suggest?"

"If you'll serve as treasurer, I'll give you twenty-five dollars, and we'll start a fund for whatever it takes, and we'll send Miss Bonnie to a school to take some piano lessons. She works pretty hard and does some things around the house and this 'n that, and maybe doesn't have the time to practice a lot. If we make up a fund and you take charge of the money and pay the bill, we'll send her to a professional piano school somewhere. That will give her a rest and also give her some training, and she'll come back here and play to your heart's satisfaction."

Mr. Bryant thought that was a splendid idea. "We'll just do that," he said.

About that time the song was over, and "Miss Bonnie" stood up. It wasn't Miss Bonnie at all; it was my wife, Geneva.

Elbert Bryant said, "A.D. Harrell, you ought to be horsewhipped here and now. I'm going home!"

Mr. Bryant turned and marched out of that church house and disappeared.

Where Did You Come From?

In the fall of 1975, some Brethren minister held a series of night services at the Pleasant Grove Church of the Brethren here on Harrell Hill. After one of those services, the congregation came outside the church. We milled around in front of the church, visiting with each other and passing the time of day for some ten or fifteen minutes. While we were talking and visiting with each other, the light in front of the church was on and we could see our way around all right. About the time we got ready to break up and walk down to where our cars were parked, about thirty yards away from the church, the light in front of the church was turned off. At that time we didn't have a security light, so we were walking in the dark.

I took Geneva by the arm and we started walking down to our car. We didn't say anything; I guess after you go to church with your wife, there's not much conversation to be engaged in, so neither one of us spoke. Just before we got to the car, the lady whose arm I was holding said, "A.D., you've got the wrong woman." Well, we had a big laugh out of that. I was walking with someone who is a real good friend of both Geneva and me.

Some ten or fifteen years later, in North Wilkesboro, North Carolina, I walked into a cafe and sat down and ordered the meal. Someone tapped me on the shoulder. I looked up and it was that fine lady that I had walked with in the dark. We were good friends before and we have remained good friends. We always get a good laugh out of that episode when we see each other.

When Geneva was a youngster, she attended the Mill Creek Brethren Church in Polk County, North Carolina, near the South Carolina line. At the time I got acquainted with Geneva, the church had a South Carolina address, Campobello, South Carolina.

One fine morning in 1989, Geneva and I decided not to go to church here on Harrell Hill, but to leave early and drive the two hours, two and a half hours, to Mill Creek Church and worship with her family and the people there. We knew the minister and about ninety-nine percent of the people there.

On this fine Sunday morning, we drove into the parking lot and as we always do on these trips, we went in through a basement door and walked through the Fellowship Hall to the hallway that goes to the bathrooms. We came first to the ladies' bathroom door, and Geneva went in. I went on down the hall for ten or fifteen feet and went into the men's room. When I came out, I walked back up to where the ladies' bathroom door opened and stood back a respectful distance to wait for Geneva to come out. When she did, I fell in step beside her.

There wasn't a great deal of light there, but there was sufficient light to see without any trouble. We walked up two flights of steps to the door to go into the sanctuary. There, the ushers gave each of us programs for the day, and we walked down the aisle.

When we go to Mill Creek, we always try to locate Geneva's family, wherever they happen to be sitting. They usually sit about two or three pews from the front of the church.

This particular day, we walked about halfway down the aisle. I had already located Geneva's family, knew where they were sitting, but Geneva didn't go up to her family. She peeled off to the left and went into a pew and sat down. After she sat down, I moved in beside her and sat down, leaving room at the end of the seat, near the aisle, for about two or three people. After we sat down, Geneva moved over about six inches to her left, closer to the man on her other side. Being the dutiful husband that I am, I moved over to the left, too, and sat fairly close to her.

About that time, the minister announced a song. I got a song-book out, and Geneva got a separate songbook, and we stood up and sang three or four verses of the song, then sat back down. At that point, Geneva again moved over to the left, three or four inches closer to the man on her left. Like the good man I am, I moved over three or four inches closer to her. I noticed at that time that the man on the other side of her looked around right straight at me like he was a little bit upset, like maybe something was wrong. I knew the man, so I nodded to him and leaned back to listen to the sermon.

About that time, somebody moved into the seat from the aisle and sat down on my right. I looked around and it was Geneva.

I don't think I have ever been more flustered in all my life. I said, "Where on earth did you come from?"

Geneva just about skinned me over that deal.

I have run into that lady two or three different times since then, and we talk about that. I was so embarrassed, though, that I don't have an awful lot to say to her about it. I know that she knew from the time I walked beside her at the restroom, walked up those steps, through the doors, down the aisle, and sat down, that I had just simply stepped in beside the wrong woman and hadn't looked, hadn't checked, and hadn't spoken to see who it was.

After church that day, I laughed and talked with her husband at some length. I had known him for a long time. I told him, "Before we come down again, I'm going to call you and tell you that we're coming and ask you to please keep your wife in tow."

Geneva's Broken Ankle

In these mountains in late October, usually from about October the fifteenth to October the twenty-fifth, the leaf color is beautiful beyond description. On one October day in 1975, Geneva and I decided to take advantage of that beautiful leaf color and drive out to a National Forest area and park our vehicle and hike to the top of one of the mountains. We did that, parked our vehicle and hiked up the side of the mountain, enjoying the beauty of the leaf color and the clear blue sky. Everything looked good.

In our hiking, we came across considerable black bear signs. We passed an apple tree or two, and the bear had eaten an apple or two. They had bedded down there, and they had left claw marks on the trunk of the apple tree where they had climbed up and down. These signs were fairly fresh, meaning they were "using" there at that time. We made proper note of that fact and kept on walking up the mountain.

We kept seeing bear tracks in the road and in the mud here and there, but at no time were we concerned for our safety. At no time were we afraid of them because black bears are real secretive creatures, and they are going to keep away from men. You are not going to see them often. They have a real keen sense of smell, and when they smell a human being they move out. We did not expect to see a bear, and didn't expect to hear a bear, although we were seeing fresh tracks.

We walked on up to the top of the mountain, probably about an hour or so, or maybe longer. We sat there on the mountain top and enjoyed the leaf color. We spoke a time or two about the bear tracks and what beautiful scenery we were seeing.

It came time to start back to our vehicle, and we started back down the mountain. We were walking in a little bit of a trail, not very rough, just a few loose rocks here and there. Geneva was one or two steps behind me and she fell down. She stepped on a rock and slid and fell. I turned around to help her up, and she said, "A.D., I have broken my ankle."

I said, "No, surely not up here on this mountain. You must just have sprained it."

"No. I broke it. I heard it break. It's broken."

We took her shoe off and looked at her ankle. It looked in bad shape. I said, "I believe you can support your weight on my arm enough for us to get out of here."

We tried that for one or two steps. The pain was unbearable for her. It was clear that that was not going to work.

I said, "I believe that if I leaned over and you put both arms around my neck and rested your weight on my shoulders, then I believe I can carry you out of here, as long as it's down hill."

We made about twenty feet like that. I could carry her, and we could have made it like that, but I could not keep that broken foot up off the ground completely. At every five or six steps, that broken foot would drag on the ground. The pain was simply more than she could bear. I had to set her down.

I said, "Let's try one other thing. Let me take my knife and go here and cut two limbs and make two crutches out of them. I'll cut them with a fork in them so you can put a crutch under each arm. We'll see if we can get you out that way."

I cut two limbs and we tried that. But that didn't work because the limbs where they forked weren't wide enough. They pinched her under the arms so much that she couldn't stand that. We agreed that the only thing to do was to make her as comfortable as possible and for me to go get help.

When we made that agreement, Geneva said, "Now you can find me when you come back, can't you?"

I said, "Yes. I won't have any trouble finding you. I can find you here in the dark, if necessary. I won't have any trouble whatsoever. Don't you worry. I won't have any trouble."

We each had on fluorescent orange hats that Farm Bureau Insurance had given us.

We made Geneva as comfortable as possible. I took off down the mountain. I had to go about two miles to get to the nearest house. I got to that house, went in, told them what the trouble was, and requested their permission to call the ambulance and the sheriff's department and so forth for help. I called the rescue squad and the sheriff's department, told them where we were and how to get to us and told them to send help.

By that time, two neighbors came in. The three of us started back to get Geneva. We took a chair to carry her in, and I insisted that we also take a blanket of some kind because I was afraid that the pain might be enough that she might go into shock and might be cold.

One of these neighbors had an old Army Jeep, and we drove it just as far as we could drive it up the side of the mountain. Then, the three of us went on walking to where Geneva was. One gentle-man, a man of about thirty, was a little bit overweight, but he got out in front, almost in a run. I called to him, "Slow down. It's too far up there to go at that speed and at that pace. You just simply can't make it at that pace."

He said, "Oh, I will. I won't have any trouble. I'm going." And he went on out of sight.

The other man and I walked along behind him at a fast pace, but at a pace I knew we could keep up and not have a heart attack or something. After about twenty minutes, we came upon the third man. He was sitting on a stump, fanning himself. His face was red as fire. He had just walked too fast and had given out, so we left him sitting there and walked on up the mountain.

When we got within fifty yards of Geneva, I saw that red hat on a stick, up about ten or fifteen feet high. I knew right then what had happened. She had been afraid that we couldn't find her, so she had taken that fluorescent hat off and put it on that stick and stuck it up to be sure that we would find her. Of course, we went straight to her.

We got her on that chair. She was in pain, she was hurting, but she wasn't in shock, so we didn't need the blanket. We put her on the chair and carried her down to the Jeep and got her in the Jeep, then carried her back down to the house where I made the tele-phone call. By that point, the sheriff's department and the rescue squad met us. We put her in an ambulance and took her to the hos-pital emergency room.

Sure enough, Geneva had a broken ankle. She stayed in the hos-pital for a week, recovering and getting that ankle straightened up.

Geneva told me afterwards that while she was on the mountain waiting for us to come back and get her (and she was there maybe an hour or an hour and fifteen minutes) that at every noise she heard she imagined it was one of those bears. She heard what was probably squirrels in the leaves and this 'n that. But she said that when anything made any noise, she thought, "Well, that's that bear coming over here." She was quite worried that the bears might find her before we did.

Shooting the Chinese Pillow

Whenever my wife purchases something at the shopping center, or at the mall, or at the supermarket, whatever she has purchased is just another item that was bought to take home. If my wife is so fortunate as to find something on the sidewalk or on the street, or on our farm here, that's just an item that she found. None of these purchases and none of these found items are particularly important.

When my wife goes to a garage sale and purchases something, then whatever she purchases is something special. A garage sale purchase has an aura about it. Purchasing something at the garage sale must give one the same feeling that the old prospectors of the gold rush times felt whenever they found a gold nugget. They have the feeling that they have really found something special.

When the garage sale purchase is brought home, it is given a special place in the house. These purchases are not to be borrowed, they are not to be moved around, and they are not to be taken out of the house. If by chance I or someone else should move one of those garage sale items, it must be put back. They are to be treated with extreme care. They are not to be defaced or scarred or messed up in any shape or form. And woe unto A.D. Harrell if he should break any of these well understood rules about garage sale items.

I went once with my wife and our daughter, maybe both of our daughters, to a garage sale in Black Mountain, North Carolina. At that garage sale, my wife bought several items. I recall a chair or two. I recall a coffee table that was of walnut, with an exquisite leather cover on the top. My wife also purchased two pillows that you would place on either end of the couch, partly for comfort and partly for decoration.

Those two pillows were stuffed with white goose feathers. The covering of the pillows was a wine-colored velvet. Those pillows were made in China, not in the sense that China or some oriental country makes something cheaper than we do here, but in the sense that it was exquisite and expensive, like you would think of fine Chinese silk. These two pillows were considered an important part of our living room decor.

With what has been said serving as a background, I looked out the back window one day in May at a field of corn that was just coming up. The little tips of corn seedlings were about an inch high. Looking out the window at the corn, I saw three or four crows that were going up, each of them going up a row, pulling up these little corn plants, destroying them. That called for some action that would get those crows out of that cornfield.

I picked up my deer rifle and put a 125-grain bullet in it, the same type of bullet that I use to shoot ground hogs on the farm. I looked around the house for something that would be soft enough to settle that rifle barrel down in while I was trying to hold a crosshair on a crow about a hundred and seventy-five yards away.

When you shoot at something that far away, special arrangements are required. With the gun barrel resting on anything hard, such as wood or stone, your heart beat and your breathing and your nerves cause the gun to vibrate just a tiny bit. And a tiny bit is too much.

The oldest grouse hunter and the youngest. A.D. Harrell and Jesse Harrell, April, 1995.

In looking for something soft to put that gun barrel on, I picked up one of these fine garage-sale pillows, pillows that were full of white goose feathers and enclosed in fine Chinese velvet.

I take this pillow out behind the house. I lay it up on the edge of the bank, on the lower side of the corn field behind the house. I sit down in a chair I carried out to make myself more comfortable. I get everything lined up and I pick out the crow that was the closest to me. It was still a hundred-and-fifty to a hundred-and-seventy yards away.

I laid that gun barrel on that pillow. I put my eye up to the telescope and I put the crosshairs on a crow. Everything was set. I squeezed the trigger.

I heard that crow caw a little. But what I saw was a snow storm of feathers between the end of my gun barrel and the crow. The valley was full of feathers.

When I put that rifle down on the pillow, the tip of the pillow, probably an inch, was actually in front of my gun barrel. When I fired, the bullet tore off the corner of that pillow. The vacuum formed by tearing off the corner of that pillow and the concussion from the rifle barrel took out about one half of the feathers.

I knew that the fat was in the fire.

I took the pillow back into the house and searched the house over for the appropriate feathers. I couldn't find any. I took me a curved needle and I found some thread that pretty well matched the color of that wine-colored velvet, then I spent half an hour very carefully sewing up the corner of that pillow. I laid it back on the end of the couch. I put the torn up part in the least obvious position, hoping it wouldn't be found. I patted the pillow down real carefully.

A little later on in the evening, Geneva came in. I got me a newspaper and I went to reading. We spoke a few words, and she laid some of her stuff down. I kept on reading. I didn't look over that paper much; I was really interested in what I was reading. Geneva sat down on the couch. I didn't say anything. I was just reading.

"What happened to the pillow?" she asked. I was still reading. I didn't hear a thing.

"What have you done to my pillow?" she asked, this time a little louder.

"Your pillow got shot."

"In the name of all that is holy, why would anyone shoot a pillow?"

I told her about the crows taking up the corn.

She had listened to me less than half a minute when she said, "I'll tell you what you need. You need to be made to eat crow at every meal for a week!"

CHAPTER SIX

Public Life

Navy Service

The Japanese bombed Pearl Harbor on December 7, 1941. I was teaching high school in Johnston County, North Carolina, at a little town called Pine Level. When President Franklin D. Roosevelt made his speech calling the bombing the day of infamy, I knew that my days of teaching were numbered. I knew that I would not continue to work as a civilian with the war going on as it was. My conscience wouldn't let me continue to work in civilian life after hearing what had happened to those Navy men at Pearl Harbor, and knowing that war would need man after man after man.

I resigned my teaching position sometime in February 1942 and went to Raleigh, North Carolina, to the Navy recruiting office and applied for enlistment in the Navy Air Corps. I was told that I would be informed sometime later on to come back to Raleigh to take the physical examinations and mental tests and so forth.

Sometime later on I got communications to go to Raleigh at such and such a date and take the physical. I recall that there were fifty-three men taking that physical. We were examined by a battery of about seven doctors: one eye specialist; one heart specialist; one ear, nose and throat specialist; and so forth. I don't remember what they all were, but there was a whole battery of them.

When the day was over, three men out of the fifty some passed all of the physicals. At that time, the enlistment requirements were much more severe than they were later. Later on, the need for men

became so great that the requirements for enlistment apparently
were lowered.

I had to go back to Raleigh a second time on that physical because on the first examination on a chart testing for color blindness
I inadvertently read a "5" for a "3". I had to go back to check that
thing out, but on the second round I read that thing correctly and
passed. I signed up with the Navy Air Corps for the remainder of
the war or as long as I would be needed.

I was told to return to civilian work to await orders. It would
take some time to process the enlistment papers. Since I was apply-
ing for enlistment as an officer, an FBI check would be made into
my background and into my suitability to serve. Those checks, I
suppose, were necessary because in the officers' ranks we would
be handling confidential and some secret information.

On May 4 1942, I received an officer's commission from President Franklin Roosevelt, signed by Frank Knox, secretary of the
Navy. The commission was as a Navy ensign.

The same package of mail also included my orders. I was
ordered to flight training at a base just outside of Atlanta, my memory says at the northern end of Peach Tree Street, Gordon Field.

Our flight training consisted of flying a training plane about two
hours each morning if the weather was satisfactory. This plane was
a two-seater biplane, a plane with two wings on each side of it. It
had two open cockpits. In the front cockpit sat an instructor with a
set of controls and a communication system to talk with the student. In the back cockpit sat the student. Both the student and the
teacher had a full set of controls. Of course with the cockpits' being
open, we had to dress for real cold weather. Depending on how
high we went, it could get real cold, so we bundled up in flight
jackets and helmets and gloves and scarves and so forth to keep
from freezing to death.

In this training plane, the controls consisted of two pedals to control the rudder of the plane, to turn it to the left or right, and what we called a joy stick, which controlled the ailerons on the wings. That joy stick came right up between the student's knees. It looked very much like the gear shift on a standard transmission truck, and you held it like you held a gear shift. If you wanted to dip the plane to the left you moved that joy stick, and if you wanted to move to the right you moved that stick. Move it to the left, the lift wing would dip; move it to the right, the right wing would dip. Thereby, you could bring your plane into a curve, along with some control from the rudder.

We received real careful instructions as to what to do each time we went up. I do not recall that we had a checklist of things to do. I think it was a process of remembering the things to do. We were to check out everything about the plane. We were to check the communication system between the student's cockpit and the instructor's cockpit. We were always to be sure to wear our helmets and gloves and so forth. And above all, we were always to fasten our safety belt and to be sure that our parachute was in place and felt comfortable to sit back against and that the rip cord was properly placed in front of our chest so if we had to bail out, we could pull that rip cord to make the parachute open.

The trainers repeatedly stressed fastening that safety belt. We were held into that plane by our safety belts. We were in an open cockpit, and all that would keep us from falling out on our heads were the fastened safety belts. Probably the last thing the trainers would tell us to do before take off was to be sure that safety belt was fastened.

After two or three months of flight training I was doing pretty well. I was out there one morning, flying at about ten thousand feet. Everything was fine as far as I could tell.

Suddenly, without any advanced warning of any kind, the instructor turned that plane upside down.

Lo and behold! I had not fastened my safety belt that morning. All I had to hold onto was that joy stick.

I held onto that thing for dear life, just praying that it wouldn't come loose. If it were to come loose, down for ten-thousand feet would go me and the joy stick, depending only on a parachute.

After a few minutes of flying upside down and my being scared beyond speaking, the instructor straightened the plane up and brought it back right side up. I can tell you exactly what he said.

His words were, "I expect you'll fasten that damn safety belt next time, won't you?"

There are a few instances that I remember from four years of Navy service, and that joy stick bit is one of them. Holding onto a little stick about as big as your thumb for dear life and not knowing if it's going to hold your weight or not is something to remember.

After I had done flight training for two or three weeks and gotten to know the other fellows in the squadron, I made a mental note that in the group of men with me the average age was somewhere between eighteen and nineteen, but I was twenty-six. Sometime after the joy stick incident, I got to comparing my reactions to flying and landing and taking off and this 'n that to my nineteen-year-old buddies. That difference in age made some difference in how we looked at our training, and how we considered the dangers of it and the Navy life in general. Their reactions were quite different from mine. They didn't see any danger. It was all one big joke, a fun thing to them. But I saw the danger in it.

Along that line I decided it would be better for me and better for the Navy if I stopped my flight training and shifted into some other field in the Navy. I went to my commanding officer and expressed my thoughts to him. I told him I thought I might be worth more in some other area, rather than as a Navy pilot. He was very understanding; they didn't want anyone flying those planes who wasn't completely satisfied with it. Because those planes cost about a million dollars, they didn't want to waste a lot of time on some student who wasn't going to make a good pilot. The commanding officer and I agreed that I would transfer to the field of communications for the Navy Air Corps. Shortly after, I received the necessary orders transferring me from flight training to communications.

About that time I went to Key West, Florida, and did three days of training in a submarine, USS-U16. We went down in that submarine to about ninety feet; we cruised usually at about seventy-five feet. That was an interesting experience, to be down under the ocean that far and to watch all the controls, the depth gauges and so forth, and to watch the depth gauges change as the submarine came back to the top. I spent three days on that submarine and three nights in Navy officers' quarters on the base at Key West.

That submarine duty was just a training activity. I just wanted to do two or three days of it to see what life was like for the men that were on a submarine. I found out and I enjoyed it. Incidentally, that's the most crowded quarters of any place I've ever been in my life. There were sixty-eight men on that submarine, and you could scarcely take a step without brushing into another sailor.

Geneva and I were married in September 1942. We maintained living quarters in Miami for the first two years of my Navy duty. After we were married and after the submarine duty, I received orders to report to a seaplane tender that was anchored off the north coast of Cuba. We were servicing a squadron of planes doing submarine search and destroy duty.

Sometime in this time span we had a visit from a USO touring group, putting on a show for the men of the services. I recall the touring group that came to our ship consisted of Bob Hope, Hedy Lamarr, one other lady (I've forgotten her name), Jerry Colonna, and Mrs. Franklin D. Roosevelt. I don't remember a thing that Bob Hope said. I don't remember a thing that Jerry Colonna said. I don't remember a thing that the young ladies said. But I do remember word for word what Mrs. Franklin D. Roosevelt said.

She said, "My husband sends greetings to you men. I bring you more than greetings. I bring you the love of your mother. I have a son in service, too. I know how your mothers feel. I feel the same way. I wish you God speed. God bless you, and as a mother to her son, here is all my love."

Those words were spoken in such a beautiful, heartfelt, and warm manner that Mrs. Roosevelt was far more outstanding in her beauty than the starlets with Bob Hope and Jerry Colonna.

Doug was born in 1943. I got to fly in to see him and Geneva for a week and then I flew back out to duty. It was shortly after that, while on seaplane tender duty, that I was promoted to lieutenant, junior grade.

Later on, I was transferred to the Isle of Pines, one hundred miles south of Cuba, as communications officer. The long abandoned citrus plantations on the Isle of Pines had more coveys of bobwhite quail than I had ever seen before. I had the bird hunting bug at that time and it was my opinion that something should be done about all the bobwhite quail.

I go to the commanding officer, Commander Hanse, and tell him about all the quail I have been seeing. I float the idea that it might be well for him to get off a communiqué to the Navy Department in Washington requesting a half a dozen semi-automatic shotguns, suitable for bird hunting. We clearly needed those shotguns in the field of rest and recreation for the troops, as we had much spare time on our hands.

The commander agreed wholeheartedly with the idea. Within two or three weeks we had in hand the shotguns requested. The requisition to Washington also included fifty cases of low brass, number eight shot, twelve-gauge shotgun shells. The shells came along with the shipment of guns, so we had them at the same time.

Navy personnel were put up in a local hotel. We slept there and we were fed by the kitchen and dining facilities of that hotel. The manager of that hotel happened to own a pointer bird dog. That bird dog was red, about the color of an Irish setter. To this day, that's the only red pointer bird dog that I have seen.

The commander and I killed a number of quail that would be illegal in the United States. We used them all by getting the local Cubans to dress them and the hotel kitchen staff to serve them at our table.

I know this is a little late, but to that Mr. Amobly who owned that bird dog, I want to say "thank you."

The commander and I usually hunted from around three o'clock to around dark. One episode on one of those evening hunts comes back to mind as clearly as if it were yesterday. (This was 1944, probably.) When a covey of quail flushed and headed for the brush, I shot four or five times. Shortly after this burst of gunfire, a Cuban man came running out of the brush, waving both arms, shouting, "Mi casa, mi casa."

The shot from my shooting had rained down on the tin roof of his house, which was hidden from us by the brush.

It was while at the Isle of Pines that I was promoted to full lieutenant. I served the remainder of my duty at San Juan, Puerto Rico, still a communications officer.

When the war was over the time came to decide whether to return to civilian life or whether to make the Navy a full-time career.

I was offered the choice of accepting promotion to lieutenant commander if I would sign up for an additional sixteen years, which would make a total of twenty years in the Navy. I didn't give that much thought. I had not seen my wife Geneva nor my son Doug since he was a few weeks old. I was getting pictures of him, and I could see here was a little boy, two and a half years old, running around, having a ball. But I couldn't hold him; I couldn't touch him. I told my senior Navy people that I was going home. I'd had enough. I'd done my duty, and the uppermost thing in my mind was to get home and see my wife and that little boy. That ended a Navy career that was full of interest and so forth, but you can get homesick.

I'll recount one homesick situation. One Christmas day, probably in 1944, in my communications barracks were seven other officers, all of us men with families. One of them was a dear friend of mine whose wife had a baby boy, after he had joined the Navy. He had never seen that baby boy. Every week, he would come to my room and say something like, "Harrell, just how does a baby boy act when he's two weeks old? . . . How does that boy act now that he's a month old? . . . Is he gurgling? Is he grunting?" This went on for two years.

This Christmas, with none of us men able to go home and see our families, we decided to celebrate anyway. We got us a big old dishpan that would hold, probably, four gallons. We bought a bunch of champagne; I don't remember how much, maybe a gallon or two. We poured that champagne in that dishpan and we finished it up with ice and eggnog. To celebrate Christmas we drank champagne. Believe it or not, it was some celebration. I didn't get dead drunk, but I did drink some champagne.

Incidentally, in all this Navy activity, seaplane tender, flying, submarine duty, I never did get seasick. I was lucky. I've seen some
men so sick they'd like to die.

One time I flew in a dirigible, or a blimp, called a K-ship, the
same type of blimp that flies over these big football games with a
Goodyear sign on it. I flew in that thing one time for eighteen
hours. I got in it at one o'clock in the morning, and we had just
had a big New Year's day meal. They have some beds in them, just
over the control section. I crawled into one of those beds. In about
thirty minutes, I was sick. I was seasick. I was airsick. I was every
kind of sick you can think of. I came down out of there and I found
me a bucket and I vomited and I vomited. That went on for eighteen hours. When that eighteen hours was over, when I stumbled
out of that blessed thing, I went to the scales and I'd lost twelve
pounds. I hadn't eaten one bite and I'd vomited everything that a
man can vomit and still live. That's another fine episode that I
remember pretty clearly.

Let me say a few things about this communications duty, the
type of work and so forth. I supervised a group of enlisted radio
men. Those men took messages that were encoded in a secret
code. They received those messages in radio Morse code and
brought them to the communications officer. With his decoding
machines and apparatus, the communications officer decoded
them and put them into English and transmitted those messages to
the proper authority, to whomever the messages were addressed.

Those radio men that I supervised were highly trained, highly
capable, fine young men. It would be a great pleasure to meet with
some of those young men again, to see how they are doing.

I recall some of the messages. I can't say much about them.
Some of them were confidential, some of them were secret mes-

sages, some of them were top secret messages. When I started decoding a message if the first word said "confidential" I went ahead
and decoded it. If it said "secret" I went ahead and decoded it and
routed it to its proper destination. If it said "top secret" then I got
another officer, and we decoded it together, then together we took
it to the designated destination. Handling those things was pretty
interesting, to say the least.

Another Circle of Life

In November 1995, I received a telephone call from Doug's son
Greg, my grandson. He says, "I want to ask you to do something
for me."

"All right. What is it?"

"This December fifteenth I receive my Army commission. I want
you to come here to Western Carolina and administer the oath that
goes with my being commissioned as an officer."

"I'll be there!"

Come December 15, 1995, at 10:15 a.m., I march onto the stage at
Western Carolina University on the right side of a splendid grandson (his father and mother are on the left side) and take part in the
ceremony making him Second Lieutenant Greg Harrell, U.S. Army.
Fifty-four years ago, in 1941, I took that same oath.

It will take a day or two, maybe three, for the swelling pride and
my head to come back down to normal size.

Stories from Years as a Teacher—Memorable Students

Teaching is a profession in which you have an opportunity to
help people that need help. I found out that you can't help everybody. You can't help everybody that you would like to help, but
there are many that you can help. From my efforts in trying to give

special attention to people, to students, that I thought needed special help, I have received many blessings.

I was raised in the community I taught in and I knew the people. I knew which families had money; I knew which families didn't have money. I knew the students who would come to school in clothes that were just barely sufficient and would have almost no money to spend. For some reason—probably because I came up through the Depression, when living was extremely hard—I did make a special effort to help students from financially deprived homes whenever I could, and there were several such students in every class.

Some of these students come to mind immediately. I remember coming from the community of Poplar two students from one family. I knew their situation because I had passed their house time and time again on some errand. I knew their parents struggled for them to get to school with sufficient clothes and sufficient money. The parents could provide barely enough for them to come to high school, so I made a serious effort to be extremely polite every time I met them in the hall, to speak to them, to smile at them.

When I had them in class, I tried to stop by their desks and give them a little extra help to let them know that I was interested in them and to let them know that the fact that they didn't have as much as some of the other students had no effect on, made no difference to, my trying to help them and on my love for them. For the four years those children were in my classes and in that high school, I did what I could to make their day a little more pleasant and to give them what help they needed.

Ten years after I quit teaching, my wife was conducting a home demonstration club meeting in the Poplar community. A lady there came up to her and said, "Now you are A.D. Harrell's wife, are you not? I want to tell you how much my children thought of Mr. Harrell. My son said, 'He treats us, Mamma, just exactly like he treats those people that have all kinds of money. He never looks down on us. He is kind to us and helps us every single time he can, just the way the rest of them are helped.'"

This came from a mother whose children had been befriended ten years before. She remembered it. I haven't seen those children since they left high school. I haven't had any contact with them. But every time I look back and think of them, I think there are two whose days I helped to make a little bit brighter. Their mother knew it, so she came to my wife and said "thank you."

There was another situation of the same nature in which a young lady named Lucy Cable came to school, and it was clear that she had just the bare necessities. One day Lucy missed school. The next day I said, "Lucy, I noticed you weren't here yesterday. I hope nothing was wrong."

She said, "No, nothing was wrong. My mother isn't living, and I am the only help my daddy has. Sometimes certain jobs come up and I have to stay out of school and help my daddy. Yesterday I helped him rake hay. I drove a team of mules and a hay rake and helped him put that hay around a hay stack."

Simply noting that she had missed had a good effect on Lucy. At every opportunity, I tried to make it clear to Lucy Cable that she was just as good as the prettiest girl and the best-dressed girl in that school. In my classes she would receive exactly the same courtesy, the same consideration, and the same attention (actually, a little more attention, if anything) as anybody else.

I had Lucy in school twenty years ago. Some year or two ago, I had a letter from her with her married name, thanking me for being helpful to her.

A young man in the same situation, his name was Buchanan, came from a log cabin. That log cabin is still standing. He came to school, I thought, under adverse conditions. I felt like he needed help and he needed some personal attention to make him feel welcome and to make him feel proud of himself. I tried to do those things with that Buchanan boy all four years of high school.

He graduated and some twenty-five years after that I was invited to a reunion of the class that he was in. He and I visited a little bit, exchanging some memories of high school days and so forth. He remembered that I had been a friend of his.

Last Christmas word came that the Buchanan boy was having some serious medical problems. That he was in the hospital and back home and back in the hospital and back home with this problem. By his brother I sent him as fine a Christmas tree as I could find on our farm. I wrote a note that there were no charges and I hoped he enjoyed it.

I got a letter from that Buchanan boy; he's a man, now, about sixty years old. He said, "I want to thank you for that Christmas tree. It's a beautiful thing. It helped make Christmas for my family and me, and I want to thank you. I want to thank you for *still* being good to me."

I appreciated his phraseology.

Another situation in our community was a young man named Royce Bryant. This Bryant boy was a neighbor of mine, close by our church here. He came to Tipton Hill High School as a freshman and he was a pretty rowdy, unruly boy. I thought he was going to have some problems because he was getting off on the wrong foot. The principal and I conferred on this Bryant boy, and both of us noted that he was pretty much of a roughneck and might be headed in the wrong direction. We agreed to try to help him and guide him along as best we could and hope that in a year he would get over this period in his life, which we called "getting over fool's hill."

The rest of those three years in high school I tried to talk to him once in a while, visit with him once in a while, ask him how things were going, ask him if I could help with anything, how were his other classes, how was he getting along and this 'n that. I showed some interest in him. He didn't respond with any "thank you" or "I appreciate it" or anything, but he did not get into trouble. He came on through high school with a good record.

Royce passed away about a year ago, and a message came to me within the last year from his parents. The boy talked to them some time before he died. He had said, "I was headed in the wrong direction, I was running with the wrong crowd, I was doing the wrong thing, I was getting involved in the wrong activities. A.D. Harrell's being kind to me and showing me that he had some interest in me gradually turned me around. I want you as my family to know how much he had to do with my being as fine a man as I have been."

I helped him twenty-five or thirty years ago. The message got back to me via his mother within the last year.

These memories are some of the most satisfactory things that have happened to me in my lifetime, just to know that you have had a positive impact, a positive effect on at least some lives. I know about these four; hopefully, there were others that I had a good influence on, too.

I'm proud of that help for an additional reason. Every once in a while, I'll come across a man of fifty or sixty years old and he'll say, "I would have finished high school except for So-and-so. I absolutely couldn't get along with that teacher, and she was after me all the time." I hope and pray that I never have to face that situation, to have some former student say that he had to quit because I wasn't good to him.

Falling Asleep in Assembly

One week at the high school, the principal was out for a week. He missed an entire week and our schedule called for, either on Wednesday or Thursday, I forget which, an assembly program with the entire school in the auditorium with a program of some assembly speaker. With the principal out, it was my responsibility to do his duties, to look after things and keep things moving. This assembly speaker, a minister from one of the local churches, a real fine gentleman, came in.

We got the assembly together, and I got up on the stage with him and made a flowery introduction for him. Told what a fine gentleman he was and where he lived; what a good speaker he was, and how we looked forward to hearing him speak and appreciated his coming to speak to us.

With that, I turned it over to him. He came on up to the podium, and I went back about two rows of seats and sat down.

The next thing I knew, some senior boy was shaking my by the shoulder and saying, "Mr. Harrell. Mr. Harrell. Wake up. Wake up! He's finished. Wake up. He doesn't know what to do."

I blundered around, wiped my eyes and this 'n that, and tried to thank the speaker again, and dismissed assembly and sent everybody back to their classes.

One of the reasons for going to sleep in the school assembly, was that I was going by a schedule that was quite time consuming and required a lot of energy and so forth. For example, a normal day

for me consisted of getting up at four o'clock in the morning, helping milk or milking fifty-six dairy cows and getting the milk parlor
cleaned up, after that, rushing to the house and taking a bath,
shaving, and getting dressed for school. I needed to be at school by
eight o'clock. From eight o'clock till three, I was involved in sched-
uling, school, and class activities and in coaching high school
athletics.

On days that we had basketball games the coming night, I
would leave the school house about three-thirty, rush home, see
about getting the cows milked, and by six-thirty be on my way
somewhere to a high school basketball game. As long as those basketball games were at the home school, no big problem. But if they
involved driving some hour or two that meant that I'd get back
home around twelve or one o'clock in the night.

I'd get in bed as fast and as soon as I could, and I'd sleep until
four o'clock the next morning, regardless of what time I got in. I'd
get up at four o'clock and go out to those cows, and I'd milk those
cows again, and back to school I'd go. When assembly came, give
me half a minute and I'd be sound asleep.

That may have been the best rest period I got in twenty-four
hours, sitting there in that general assembly with five hundred
kids around me, dead to the world. I didn't have any worries of
conscience or anything and I could sleep anywhere that I could sit
down and rest a minute or two.

Unfortunately, that sleeping in assembly tended, and still does
tend, to carry over in the church services. I have to watch myself
real carefully or I'll sit there looking the preacher in the eye and listening as close as I can listen and the first thing I know I'll be
sound asleep and Geneva will be punching me and punching me
and waking me up 'cause I've gone to sleep again.

Marshall Street

In the section about splitting the black gum tree and pulling the baby through (chapter five), I mentioned that a gentleman named Marshall Street cut down that tree in 1990 and worked it through his sawmill operation. I want to say some other things about Marshall Street. Marshall is the number one sawmill operator and timber man in this part of Mitchell County. He is known far and wide for his honesty, for his fairness, and for his integrity in dealing with the people that he buys timber from. My first contact with Marshall Street was in 1958. He walked into my classroom at Tipton Hill High School as a tall, black headed freshman. He went out for basketball and eventually made an outstanding player.

Marshall has always spoken real softly, real slowly, real carefully, evidently weighing every word. One time during basketball practice I had stepped outside or turned my back to what was happening on the floor for some reason. When I came back in, a young man named Gene said Marshall had hit him, and his face showed he had been treated pretty roughly. I called Marshall over to see what was going on.

I said, "Marshall, did you hit him?"

"Yes. I hit him."

"What did you hit him for?"

"I went in to shoot a basketball goal, and he laughed at me, so I hit him."

"Did you hit him very hard?"

"Yes. I hit him pretty hard. I knocked him down."

"We can't afford to have this kind of stuff going on in here. Right now I don't have the time to fool with you two boys; I've got to load some buses out here. In the morning, both of you come to my classroom about ten minutes to eight, before classes start. I'm going to give both of you five licks with that paddle that lays on my desk. See you tomorrow."

The next morning at fifteen till eight, not ten till eight, Marshall came into my room. He walked up to me and said, "Mr. Harrell, if it's all right with you, I would rather that the principal paddle me, rather than you."

"Marshall, I don't understand that. I want you to tell me the reasons why you'd rather the principal to paddle you as for me to paddle you."

"Everybody tells me that you like Gene a lot better than you do me and that you'd paddle me harder than you'd paddle Gene."

"Well, now. If that's the way you feel about the situation, let's just not paddle anybody. Let's forget about the whole deal. You go on to your classes and get along fine and be a good boy. Let's just forget that paddling situation completely."

Marshall went on through high school and made a fine basketball player for me. I think he could jump the highest of any boy I ever saw in my life. Down through the years after I quit teaching, Marshall took over the sawmill operation that his father had run for a long time. His father passed away, and Marshall took over the entire operation.

In that sawmill operation, Marshall has done me some favors once in a while. I remember I once took a walnut log to that sawmill, and he ripped it up into two-inch slabs. Geneva and I used those two-inch slabs to make some fine walnut furniture for our home here. Marshall sawed some other things for me a time or two, and he would never let me pay him. When I tried to pay him, he would say, "You've always been awfully good to me, and I'm glad to be able to do something for you."

In 1991, Marshall's son was unfortunate enough as to have a serious highway accident down in the state of Tennessee. The situation got in the court system in Tennessee. Marshall was real worried about him. One day Marshall came to me and said, "A.D., would you consider going down to Tennessee when that court trial comes off and see if you can help me any?"

My response was, "Marshall, I'll go any time. Give me a few hours advance notice, hopefully twelve, but not necessarily twelve. But just let me know when that court hearing is coming, where it is, and I'll drop everything I'm doing and I'll be there."

The court hearing came about. Marshall let me know just when it was happening.

I went to Tennessee and sat in the courtroom of the Superior Court of the State of Tennessee for some few hours while the hearing was going on. The courtroom was full of people, I'd say some thirty people, who had come down from the Buladean area and from the Harrell Hill area to Tennessee to support Marshall Street and his son in the legal situation. Several people in that courtroom stood up and told the judge and jury what an outstanding, honest man Marshall is and what an honest, hardworking man is the son who had the wreck. We begged the judge in his wisdom to go easy on Marshall's son. The judge listened to those requests from the citizens of this area. He said he would give that young man the minimum penalty required under the state law. The judge gave the young man permission to come back to North Carolina and do community work. The load was lifted off the shoulders of Marshall and his entire family when the judge gave his verdict.

Marshall to this day appreciates the support of all the people who went down to Tennessee. That is a concrete example of the belief that if you do the right thing, if you are fair and honest, favors will return themselves time and time again.

Basketball at Tipton Hill High School

I have referred earlier to coaching athletics at Tipton Hill High School. Now I don't put the same importance on athletics that I put on a student's making good grades or a student's being able to stand up in front of a classroom and give a report and being able to speak and think while on his feet. I don't put the importance on athletics that the general public today puts on athletics. Athletics are just not that important in the life of a child. The important things are things other than athletics.

Athletics does have a place, though. It gives some youngsters a chance to do good in some field, and it gives them a chance to be proud of themselves when they might have difficulty performing in other areas in a manner that would bring pride to them. And athletics does give them some feeling of confidence. Therein lies, in my opinion, the value of athletics.

One other value is the exercise and the physical conditioning athletics provides to the young body of the growing youngster. Years after I coached at Tipton Hill, I sometimes went with other school board members to classrooms over Mitchell County. I was appalled at the lack of good physical conditioning that I saw among those students. Time after time I saw students who were overweight, who lacked in physical conditioning. It was clear that they would have been well served to have spent some time on a football field or a basketball court and build up some muscles and some stamina and loose some of the extra weight that they were carrying. It is those areas, in my opinion, that athletics has its major points.

Mitchell County had three high schools at the time that I was coaching, from about 1948 to 1960. Those three high schools were Tipton Hill High School at Tipton Hill, Bowman High School at

Bakersville, and Harris High School at Spruce Pine. Tipton Hill was the smallest of the three. Bowman High School at Bakersville was second in size. Combined, Bowman and Tipton Hill had half as many students as did Harris High School in Spruce Pine.

Those schools competed fiercely in the field of athletics. Any time Bowman or Tipton Hill was playing Harris at Spruce Pine, Tipton Hill tended to support Bowman High and in return Bowman tended to support Tipton Hill against Harris High, simply because of size differences among the schools.

I recall even to this day one particular basketball game that Tipton Hill played on the Harris High court at Spruce Pine. Near the end of the game with Harris High, with seventeen seconds to go, Harris High was leading by a score of eighty-five to eighty. We had just scored and it was Harris High's time to put the ball in play under our basket. We called time out and had a short conference. The instructions to my team were to step up the defense and to make every effort to see to it that the men they were guarding did not receive the ball when Harris High threw it in. Our only chance was to steal the ball on the inbound pass. We were going to guard every player who was a possible receiver to keep him from receiving that ball, which would give us a chance to take the it.

Harris High threw the ball in, the score eighty-five to eighty. Our men put the defensive pressure on and took the ball. We scored, making the score eighty-five to eighty-two. Again, it was time for Harris High to throw the ball in. With the same instructions, our team put the defensive pressure on again and for the second time they took the ball and scored, making the score eighty-five to eighty-four, with seven seconds left.

For the third time in a row, Harris High threw in the ball, and for the third time in a row, a Tipton Hill man stole the pass. For the third time in a row, we scored on the play, making the score eighty-six, Tipton Hill, to eighty-five, Harris High, with three seconds to go.

Harris High called time out. My wife, who went with me to just about all of these basketball games and frequently served as assistant, happened to be sitting close enough to where they huddled to overhear their conversation. She told me what they said, after we got home that night. The coach was telling them what to do to avoid losing that ball on an inbound pass. During that conversation, the center for Harris High School spoke up loud enough for my wife to hear him say, "They'll beat us! They always beat us."

With three seconds to go, I instructed my team to let up on the defense, pick up the Harris High players at the center court, let them throw the ball in unimpeded, and not foul them. We didn't think they could get that ball down the court and score a basket within three seconds.

That's exactly what happened: Time ran out before they could score. We were a real happy and hilarious bunch of boys from Tipton Hill.

Tipton Hill High School is no longer in being in Mitchell County, nor is Bowman High School in Bakersville or Harris High School in Spruce Pine. In recent years, the high schools have been combined into one high school, located in Ledger, North Carolina. In that high school is a major trophy case that contains the trophies of the athletic teams of all three of the earlier high schools. In that trophy case are several trophies won by the Tipton Hill teams during the years that I was lucky enough to be coaching them.

Some of these Tipton Hill teams won the Toe River Valley Conference championships. Some of them went through a schedule of twenty-six games without losing a single game. The trophies in the Mitchell High trophy case speak to these figures. These victories came at a time when Tipton Hill was the smallest school in number of students attending of any school in the Toe River Valley Conference, which included the schools of Avery, Yancey, and Mitchell counties.

I don't put this segment in to be bragging about my coaching. I put it in to pay tribute to the fine young men and the fine young women who played basketball for me for the twelve years I was at Tipton Hill High School. I want especially to pay tribute to Roy Phillips, Darrell Slagle, Gibbs Stanley, and J.C. Street. They were four of the finest basketball players that any coach could be blessed with. In the Girls Division, I want to pay tribute to Alice Byrd, Jean Byrd, Juanita Harrell, Carol Harrell, Trula McCurry, and Jackie Slagle. The same thing could be said for these young ladies as for the young men. They had special talents and would have been a blessing for any coach to have on his team.

Board of Education

I worked for twenty years as a high school teacher. After retiring from teaching, I ran for the Mitchell County Board of Education and won one of five elected seats. The remaining four members elected me to serve as chairman of that board for two separate two-year terms, for a total of four years. As chairman of the board, it was my responsibility to call the board together and keep some orderly process of discussion and call for votes and set agendas and so forth.

Norris Masters also served on the school board when I did, and together we accomplished much more than either one of us could have accomplished alone. Norris and I grew up in the same community, in the same church, and we have both been involved in an agricultural economy. On top of that, we have always been good friends. For four years, we backed each other up almost one hundred percent.

In many cases, a board of education is a no-win situation for its members. For example, at one board meeting, a local doctor came in and took us, the board, to task for not having a tennis team. He wanted Mitchell County High School to have a tennis team and play interscholastic tennis because his son was interested in tennis, because his son was a pretty good tennis player. The doctor and his son played tennis on their own tennis court at home for recreation. We told him we'd take it under advisement, talk about it, see what we could do.

At the next meeting another doctor came in. He had heard we were thinking about spending money to put in a tennis program. He was all opposed to it because his son didn't play tennis. This doctor wanted us to put in a soccer program because the town that he and his family came from had a soccer team and his son was pretty good on the soccer team. He wanted us to put in soccer so his son could continue to play soccer.

That's just a simple example of how impossible it is to please everybody.

On another occasion, the father of a student at the high school came in. His boy wasn't doing too well. The father held the fact that the son wasn't doing well against one of the math teachers. He demanded that the board of education fire that math teacher.

We got to questioning the situation and asked him, the father, if his son passed that math course. He had, with a "C". Another board member asked how many days his son missed that year. The father said he had missed thirty-seven days.

Now, that number of absences is sufficient to fail the whole grade, but the boy passed.

The father continued to demand that we fire the teacher, but of course we pretty much ignored him. The father went so far as to write the State Department of Education in Raleigh, condemning this math teacher (who I thought at the time and still think today was an excellent math teacher), trying to get the state to put pressure on us to fire this math teacher.

These are just some examples of the many cases where there's no way to win serving on the board of education. You make enemies, it seems like, regardless of what you do on that board.

Some pluses I can think of. For example, on one Saturday afternoon a man by the name of Moffitt came to my house. I hadn't met the man before, but I knew who he was, and I knew that he came from the Buladean community. He came in and told me what his name was. We shook hands then visited for a few minutes.

He said, "My daughter graduated from East Tennessee State University two years ago and has a teaching certificate for the state of North Carolina. She's qualified and certified to teach in any elementary school in this county. For two years, we've not made one bit of progress getting her a job anywhere. She's never had an interview, she's never been called in, we've just been up a brick wall. If you possibly can, I want you to try to help us."

I said to "Mr. Moffitt, We have a board meeting next Monday night, some two days away from now, and I'll see what I can do. I won't forget you. I'll see what I can do."

I convened that board meeting. Sometime in the process of that board meeting, I spoke to the superintendent along these lines, "I've noticed in the past year or two that it seems like ninety-nine percent of the employment recommendations you make to this board are for people from the town of Spruce Pine. I fail to find almost any recommendations from you to employ people from Tipton Hill, from Buladean, or from Harrell Hill."

Under state law, the board of education cannot initiate any action along personnel lines. Such an action has to first come in the form of a recommendation from the county superintendent, then the board of education takes up that recommendation and can either vote it up or vote it down. But the board cannot make the recommendation.

I said to the superintendent, "Isn't it true that most all of your recommendations are for people from Spruce Pine to be hired in the school system? You have ignored, in my opinion, applications that come from Tipton Hill, Buladean, and Harrell Hill."

He said, "Well, I don't know about that. I didn't realize that."

I said, "That's my opinion, and I want to clear something with you right now. The next opening that comes in this school system, and you come before this board to make a recommendation to fill that opening, to hire a teacher to fill that opening, I want that recommendation to be for some applicant that lives in Buladean, or Tipton Hill, or Harrell Hill, providing that they have the qualifications for the job that comes up. Now do you understand what I'm driving at? I want that done the very next recommendation that you make."

He said, "Yes. Yes. I understand."

Before that meeting was over the superintendent said that a fourth grade teacher from Tipton Hill was leaving. The teacher's husband had been transferred to another job, and she was leaving with him. We had to fill the vacancy in the fourth grade at Tipton Hill the next day, which was to be her last day. We had to have a new teacher in the class Wednesday morning.

I said that was fine, I wanted to hear his recommendation.

He stood up and said, "Gentlemen of the board, I recommend that the fourth grade teacher at Tipton Hill be Miss Moffitt from Buladean."

We voted on it. She got five votes and had a job. Her father came to me on Saturday, we had the meeting on Monday, and she went to work on Wednesday. To this day when I run across that young lady, she runs up to me and gives me a big kiss on the cheek and says thank you. To this day when I see her father, he comes grinning all over, with his hand stuck out, and saying, "I didn't know you could do it that fast."

School Bus for the Canipe Children

At one of our board of education meetings, a father and a mother named Mr. and Mrs. Canipe appeared and requested that a school bus route be established in their area so the school bus might pick up their three or four children and take them to Tipton Hill School. They commented that their children were walking to and from school every day of the school year. Their request was that the walking come to an end and that we send a bus to pick up those children. There were one or two, I believe two, other families that had some children on that particular road.

I knew about Mr. Canipe's request because when I was teaching at Tipton Hill, I saw him and his brothers and sisters (and I believe there were about nine of those children) walk to that school every day, winter, summer, spring, fall, every day that they came. And they walked in rain, snow, wind, and sun. I knew that those Canipe children came to school some days with their feet wet, with their clothes wet—at least partially so—from having walked to school. They would sit there in those school rooms until their feet dried and their clothes dried. I watched that for the twelve years that I taught at Tipton Hill and I had a concern about it. I was concerned for the welfare of those children.

They were having to walk because the law in North Carolina at that time said if you live as close as one half a mile to the school which you attend, then you cannot ride the bus. You have to provide your own transportation or get there the best you can. Bus transportation was provided for all that lived farther than half a mile away from the schoolhouse.

The Canipes lived a little less than half a mile from Tipton Hill School, which meant all those children had to walk. They were a fine group of children, but they had really endured the weather. The family wasn't able to afford a car, a private car, to take them to school and drive them home. Their parents just couldn't afford that, so those children walked.

I talked to those children about it a time or two and I talked to their parents, along these lines, "If I ever have an opportunity to do anything toward getting a bus on your road so those children don't have to walk, I'll do it. I'll keep that in the back of my mind, and if opportunity ever presents itself, I'll remember that I knew you walked to school. I'll see if I can't help you."

So that night Mr. and Mrs. Canipe presented their request to the board and left the meeting. After they left I told the other board members and the superintendent what I had seen for twelve years.

I turned around to our superintendent and said, "If these board members agree, let's see if we can't send a school bus down there in the morning." We talked over the situation, that it would involve changing somebody's bus route, that it would involve calling some bus driver and telling him to extend his route the next day to get his bus down there.

In the final analysis, we worked that rerouting out. The superintendent assured us that the next morning there would be a bus on that road to pick up those children.

At eight o'clock the next morning, the school bus went down that road, turned around, came back up by Mr. Canipe's, stopped, and his four children walked out of the door, across the lawn, and into the school bus, for the first time in the lifetime of two generations there.

The next time I saw Mr. Canipe, he said, "A.D., I didn't expect you to act that fast. I didn't expect the board to act that fast."

I laughed and told him, "If you don't want something done, don't ask Norris Masters and me to tackle it. We had enough support on that board to do it, and we're just tickled to death for you."

Every time I see Mr. Canipe and his children to this day we give each other a big smile and a pat on back and are all happy that no longer does that group of children have to walk through the rain and snow to get to school.

So, there are a few pluses to being on the board of education. If you want an education, go to school, high school, then go to college and then get on the board of education and you'll see how things operate.

Rebuilding the Road between Bakersville and Spruce Pine

Sometime around 1920 a road was built from the town of Bakersville to Spruce Pine. Although it was a paved road, it snaked around and around. It seemed like the builders tried to come close to every house in the area. It was extremely hard to drive. In late years standard tractor-trailer rigs had trouble on that road, it was so crooked.

The county commissioners complained to the State Highway Department in Raleigh, asking for help in getting that road rebuilt from Bakersville to Spruce Pine. Numerous local citizens complained to the State Highway Department in Raleigh. But nothing happened.

One time, in the city of Morganton in Burke County, I came across our United States senator, Senator Sam Ervin. I approached him and talked to him about the road between Spruce Pine and Bakersville. He knew about it. He had traveled that road electioneering, and he knew how bad it was. I asked him if he couldn't help us a little. His answer completely surprised me. He said, "When you people in Mitchell county learn how to vote, we'll build you a road." I was taken aback and didn't make any progress.

I knew that since its formation sometime in the 1800s, Mitchell County had sent a Republican representative every two years to the convening of the General Assembly in Raleigh. In the state of North Carolina at that time the Democratic Party was in complete control of the whole state governmental apparatus, from the governor on down to little jobs in the Highway Department, down to the local counties and local communities. I don't think there had been a Republican in the governor's mansion in Raleigh from the time of the Civil War up until a year or two after this story that we're talking about took place. To get things done, you had to be able to work through the Democratic Party apparatus.

Years after the meeting with Senator Ervin, probably in the early 1960s, during Terry Sanford's term as governor (1961 to 1965), I served as chairman of the Republican Party in Mitchell County. This particular year when I was serving as chairman of the Republican party in the county, the Democrats in Mitchell County put up a candidate for the General Assembly named Ernest Poteat. He was an ex-banker and just an excellent, fine citizen. I got the wheels to turning and thought that here there might be a way to get that road from Bakersville to Spruce Pine resurveyed, regraded, rebuilt, and straightened out.

I called Mr. Poteat one day and said, "I want you and the chairman of the Democratic Party and your campaign manager to come to my house tonight or tomorrow night, whichever is convenient with you. I want you to come after dark. I don't want anybody to see you, but I want to talk to you."

He seemed real interested, and we set up a time for them to meet with me.

At the appointed time they came. We visited awhile, then I said, "Now here's something that I want to run by you. Gentlemen, I invited you here tonight because I have a proposition that I want to run by you. I want you to consider it, see what you think. Let me know what your feeling is.

"I'm prepared to make this proposition to you. If you, Mr. Poteat, will go to Raleigh sometime in the next ten days or so and get an audience with the governor, if you can get him to write a letter—got to put it in writing—that if we send you as a Democratic representative to Raleigh to represent Mitchell County this fall, then he as governor of the state of North Carolina would see to it that the State Highway Department builds a modern road from Bakersville to Spruce Pine. I would be able, with the help of our executive committee, to swing enough Republican votes to you to cause you to win. If Governor Sanford writes you this letter, I don't want the letter myself, for my files. I don't need it. You can keep the letter, but I do want to see it. If you can get such a letter from our governor, then I'll see to it that we elect you as the Mitchell County representative and send you to Raleigh this fall."

The gentlemen were real interested in the proposition. Their comment was, "We'll go to Raleigh, we'll talk with the governor, and we'll get back to you and let you know what he says."

Some week to ten days later, those gentlemen called me and said they wanted to come back down and meet with me again. We set up a time and they came for another night meeting. They had a letter from the governor. In this letter, the governor promised that if Ernest Poteat, a Democrat, came to Raleigh to the General Assembly to represent Mitchell County in the coming fall, then the Highway Department would build a modern road from Bakersville to Spruce Pine.

I met with the executive committee of the Mitchell County Republican Party and pointed these things out: that the road between
Bakersville and Spruce Pine was real bad, real poor, real low quality and it was holding down all kinds of progress, all kinds of development for the county and as far as I could tell, this was one
possibility of getting that new road built. They agreed with me and
my thinking that a new road for Mitchell County would be worth
far more than sending any Republican representative to Raleigh.
After all, if we could send this Democratic representative down
there and as a result get our road built, then any time in the future
we could reverse and send our Republican representative in the
years to come.

As time went by and things began to fall in place, we elected a
Democratic representative. He went to Raleigh, and our governor
was true to his promise. Within a few weeks, a few months at
most, Highway Department survey crews were at work between
Bakersville and Spruce Pine, surveying a new road. Within three or
four years that road was rebuilt, paved, and in operation. It is now
Highway 226 and has opened up Mitchell County in a manner that
we had been unaccustomed to before.

This was a job that entailed some pain, some consideration. As
chairman of the Mitchell County Republican Party, it was my im-
plied responsibility to help elect Republican representatives. But I
was turning around and helping to elect a Democratic representative. The man that we were running on the Republican ticket
was being let down. It was my judgment, and the committee
agreed with me, that if you couldn't use politics to get done what
was best for every person in the county, be he Democrat, Republican, black, white, red, or what, if you couldn't use politics to get
done what was best for all of those people, then I for one needed
to use my time and energy for something besides politics. We let
these considerations override considerations for our own party

candidate. In the final analysis he agreed with us. And he agrees with us to this day that the new road was worth more than his going to Raleigh.

An amusing incident happened in relation to that road and to the plans, the schemes, to get the road built. We had in Raleigh at that time as secretary of state for the state of North Carolina a gentleman named Thad Eure. Mr. Eure had served as secretary of state for the state of North Carolina longer than any man in the United States had served in that office for his state. Mr. Eure was a man of some importance, and he was the senior member in the Democratic Party in the state of North Carolina, in age and maybe in influence.

After he got word of the plan to send Mr. Poteat to Raleigh as the Democratic representative, Mr. Eure made this comment on a radio talk show in Raleigh, "If a Democrat comes to Raleigh to represent Mitchell County, then I will go to Bakersville, and I'll get me a mule, and I'll get on that mule, and I'll ride that mule around the courthouse square in the city of Bakersville to celebrate the Democrats finally winning one political race in that county."

From that radio talk show the Raleigh paper, *The News and Observer*, picked up those comments and ran them. Then our local paper in Spruce Pine picked them up from the Raleigh paper and ran them. I read the comments of Mr. Eure with a great deal of interest and fun. I called the Raleigh newspaper and told them who I was and that I had read with great interest Mr. Eure's plans to come to Bakersville and ride his mule around the courthouse square. I pointed out that I thought that would be unwise, that I didn't think Mr. Eure ought to do that. It was my opinion that the good people of Mitchell County might have some difficulty determining which one was Mr. Eure and which one was the mule.

That word got back to Mr. Eure, and we had a big laugh over it. He never did come to Bakersville and ride that mule, though.

Dairy Farming and
Establishing the North Carolina Milk Commission

We set up a grade A dairy operation here at Harrell Hill in 1960. We marketed that milk through the Biltmore Dairy Company, a distributor in Asheville, North Carolina. The distributor packaged that milk and distributed it to retail outlets across western North Carolina and South Carolina.

The first year that we were in the dairy business, we put that milk in cans, in ten-gallon cans, and cooled the milk in a cooler in the milk parlor here. Every other day, I put cans of milk in the trunk of my car and hauled that milk to a spot in Yancey County where I met a truck from the Biltmore Company. I switched those cans of milk to that truck to be taken on to the distributor's plant.

By the second year, I had been able to talk another farmer or two into getting in the dairy business. After a period of about three or four years, we had in Mitchell County a total of twenty-three grade A dairy farms, each of them milking cows under grade A dairy rules and regulations, subject to inspection any day and every day, and shipping milk to Biltmore Dairy.

After a few years we switched from putting the milk in cans and bought stainless steel bulk tanks. We would pour that milk directly into a tank and cool it with the refrigeration unit built into the tank. At that time a local man purchased a tanker truck and came to each farm and picked up the milk that had been produced on that farm for the previous two days. He weighed the milk each time he picked it up and took a sample of the milk to be tested in a laboratory for certain requirements. He weighed that milk by a calibrated instrument on a dip stick that he put down into the stainless steel tank. He took a sample of the milk into the laboratory at the Biltmore plant in Asheville to be checked for butter fat and to be checked by the health department for bacteria, leukocytes, and any foreign material. Incidentally, it was my experience over the twenty-two years that we were in the grade A dairy business, that those dairy farmers were the most careful and the finest producers that I have ever seen in the agricultural economy. They were extremely careful and consistently produced a high quality product for the consumer.

We paid for hauling that milk by having the receiving station take out a small amount from our check, depending on the number of hundreds of pounds of milk that the hauler had hauled for us in a month.

It's interesting to note here that when you buy and use milk, it is in gallons and quarts and pints and half pints. We dairy producers sold our milk not by gallons or pints, but by the hundreds of pounds. We were paid so many dollars for a hundred pounds. My memory says that when we first started selling milk we received about eight dollars per hundred weight. As inflation took hold, the price gradually went up until when we went out of the dairy business some twenty-two years later, the price was up to about thirteen dollars per hundred weight. We have been out of the dairy business for some time and I'm not sure what the exact price per hundred weight is in 1994. I do happen to know that it is not as high was it was when we quit some twelve or fifteen years ago. Dairy producers now are getting somewhere in the vicinity of eleven dollars per hundred weight for their milk.

I mentioned that we were paid something like eight dollars per hundred weight of milk. That figure doesn't mean that we were paid eight dollars for each hundred pounds of milk that we

shipped in. We were paid for that milk on the basis of a compli-
cated formula. I'll explain it as simply as I can here. One thing that
determined how much you got for that milk was the butterfat content of it. The higher the butterfat content of the milk, the more
you got for it. The butterfat content didn't push up the price a
great deal, maybe one or two cents per hundred for a percentage
point of increase in the amount of butterfat.

If the distributor was able to sell to the retail market all of the
milk that he took in one month—say a million pounds—from one
producer, then the producer was paid on the basis of the butterfat
in his milk, for all of the milk he produced in that particular month.
If the distributor was able to sell to the retail market only ninety
percent of the milk, then the producer was paid less for the remaining ten percent. In reality, that ten percent of unsold milk
went into the ice cream"making trade or the powdered milk trade.

We called the milk that was sold for drinking purposes class one
milk. It received the top price, with butterfat considered. Milk that
was sold for making powdered milk and ice cream was called class
two milk. To further complicate the formula, some milk was sold to
military bases. That milk was paid for at a price somewhere between the price for class one and for class two milk.

The producer was paid on a formula based on at least four considerations: the butterfat content, the amount of milk sold as class
one, the amount of milk sold as class two, and the amount of milk
sold to the military.

Another factor in that formula had to do with the amount of
milk base that the dairy producer happened to hold. For some
years, we dairy producers were in a race to see how much milk we
could produce and how much milk we could sell. In that race to
produce the most milk from each farm, we began to build up a surplus. That surplus affected the total price we got for the milk because a larger percentage of it went for class two purposes.

We set up a dairy organization in western North Carolina that had over 270 producers as members. If you draw a line through the state from north to south through Winston-Salem, from Winston-Salem west you have the area covered by our dairy organization, which consisted of the dairymen in that western area. The first president of that organization was a dairy farmer from Rutherford County. I happened to be the vice president of that organization. We had a board of directors consisting of about fifteen or twenty men from the western counties of North Carolina.

Some people think of men engaged in agriculture as having strong backs and weak minds, what some may term as rednecks. But I want to point out that these men were keen of mind. They were thoughtful, they were considerate, they were able, and they were industrious. Most of them were financially successful; in the group were three or four millionaires. They knew their way around. When we had a business meeting in Asheville or in Raleigh, or in Shelby, or wherever, you couldn't tell the group of dairymen from the bankers in the restaurant at lunch time. That was always a matter of pride to me.

We called an area-wide meeting of our organization in the early 1960s and discussed the dairy situation and decided we were foolish to be competing with each other to see how much milk we could produce. There was just a certain amount of market out there, just a certain amount of milk could be consumed, and to flood that market tended to do serious economic damage to all of us. We got our heads together and decided to ask the North Carolina General Assembly to set up a milk commission to oversee the total dairy industry in the state of North Carolina.

There was an additional reason for us milk producers to want a milk commission set up. The distributor of the milk, the company that bought the milk from us and packaged it and marketed it and sold it in retail outlets, had a tremendous amount of power over every producer. The distributor could say to a producer, I don't need your milk today; I'm not going to take it today. One or two days of that treatment would ruin some dairymen. You can't turn a thousand dollars worth of milk down the drain many times in a row and survive economically.

So, we asked the North Carolina General Assembly, through our local representatives, to set up a milk commission. Our local representatives told us to work through our dairy organization to draw up exactly what we wanted this milk commission to do, what we wanted it to be, and what authority we wanted it to have. They said that they would look at what we developed and see what they could do under the law. Any proposal had to be constitutional and had to meet several other legal and judicial requirements.

We were told to sit down around the table in our dairy organization and decide just what we wanted the legislature to do. We dairy producers were in the business of milking cows, growing feed for those cows, providing pasture for those cows, producing milk, and selling milk. Now, we were moving into a new area, preparing draft legislation, that required some careful consideration. We were moving into an area that we were not really familiar with, so we had to move real carefully.

In our meetings to decide what we wanted the legislature to do, we came up with these ideas: to set up the milk commission under the North Carolina Department of Agriculture; to give the commission the legal authority to supervise the entire grade A dairy industry from the time the milk leaves the farm until it is purchased by a consumer. That meant the proposed milk commission would be supervising the distributor as well as the producer. That milk commission was to have definite authority. No longer could a distributor without reason cut off a producer. No longer could a distributor say, "I didn't make any money last month; I'll have to be a little late in paying you."

We wanted that milk commission to set up a base system whereby each farmer would be allotted a particular base of so many hundred pounds of milk. (By a base I mean now the amount of milk that a man can produce per month and expect to sell in the class one market. This base would affect payment to the producers.) We also wanted a method set up for a new producer to come into the market. We wanted it to be that when a new producer came into the market, he could sell all his milk the first month as class two milk. The next month, a percentage of the new producer's milk would go into class one. The percentage of class one milk would increase each month until by the end of twelve months a proper percentage of the new producer's milk (the same percentage as other grade A producers) would be in the class one market.

This base we had reasons for setting up and the reasons were along this line: If a man in Mitchell County, for example, had a base of 78,000 pounds of milk and a man in Buncombe County (where the distributor was located) had a base of 78,000 pounds and on down the line, that put those men on an equal footing. If one of those men decided to double his output above his base, he would be penalized by having to sell the additional milk in the class two market. (Incidentally, this base system stabilized the dairy industry, and it's somewhat the same type of situation as the tobacco base among our local farmers.)

Our group recommended to the General Assembly, through our local county representatives, that a North Carolina Milk Commission be set up, that a majority of members be from the general public, and that one member be from the producers, one from the distributors, and one from the retailers. We presented an outline to our legislators, and the General Assembly took it from there and came up with the original North Carolina Milk Commission. The wisdom of the General Assembly was for the governor to appoint all the members.

In a period of three or four or five months, at least one session of the General Assembly, those proposals were written into the law of North Carolina. The appointments were made and the North Carolina Milk Commission became a thing of action and supervision for the entire industry. These things were taking place in 1961 to 1962.

This milk commission functioned admirably for a long time. It had a lot of challenges. It's been challenged in court, it's been considered unconstitutional a time or two, but those challenges were thrown out of court and that milk commission continued to function as long as we were in the dairy business.

After leaving the field of education, I gave more time and energy to our grade A dairy operation and in particular to our grade A dairy organization. I mentioned before that a gentleman from Rutherford County was the president and I was the vice president. That went on for a period of six or eight years. Eventually, our president went out of the dairy business. We held an election for a replacement, and there were the names of three or four capable men on the ballot, in addition to my name. I thought each of them was more capable than myself and I still think so. When the balloting was counted, 276 men had elected me as president of the dairy organization.

The milk commission, of course, was a small part of the government of the state of North Carolina. For one hundred years plus, the state government had been in the hands of the Democratic Party. This milk commission was made up of nine members of the Democratic Party, appointed by people who were members of the Democratic Party and who held important positions in the state government.

Those men on that commission were fine, outstanding, upright gentlemen, and they were all Democrats. But here, the largest dairy producers organization in the state of North Carolina had elected as president a man who is a solid Republican. We didn't have any conflicts, however, anywhere down the line. Everything ran real well.

In 1971 or '72, it looked like there might be a possibility of electing a Republican governor, a man named James E. Holshouser, from Boone in Watauga County, North Carolina. We had a feeling that Mr. Holshouser might win, so I went to his law office in Boone to feel him out about his thinking on the North Carolina Milk Commission. Mr. Holshouser told me in a real kindly, friendly manner that he felt like the price of milk was too high. It was his observation that there were babies, youngsters, whose parents absolutely couldn't afford to buy milk at the price current then. There were youngsters going without milk because the price was so high. He thought the price to dairy farmers ought to be cut down so that everybody could afford to buy milk.

I took the opposite position in that if we cut down the price of milk to the farmer, farmers would go out of the milk business and there would be less milk, driving up prices even higher.

The man who was running for governor, the men on our board of directors of our dairy organization, and myself looked at that situation differently. I couldn't move Mr. Holshouser any in his opinion of it, and he of course couldn't move me.

As time went by, Mr. Holshouser was elected governor. Subsequently, the entire North Carolina Milk Commission was replaced by new people in an orderly, efficient manner.

Now, as it developed historically after the milk commission was set up, each time the governor appointed a man to represent the producers segment of the dairy economy, he appointed a man from the producer organization of which I was president. In actual practice over a period of some years, our organization in conjunction with the state-wide Dairy Committee of the North Carolina Farm Bureau Federation would submit a list of three producers to the governor, and he had always picked someone from our group.

After Mr. Holshouser became governor, I received a telephone call one night, about nine o'clock. It was the governor's appointment secretary calling me from Raleigh. (I thought it was unusual for someone to be calling from Raleigh at that time of night.) He wanted to know if I would serve on the North Carolina Milk Commission if the governor saw fit to appoint me.

I had given Mr. Holshouser a sizeable contribution for his campaigning, and he knew about it. Also, he knew of my position in relation to the dairy organization. I told the person who called me that I was flattered, that I would consider it, and that I would call on my board of directors and tell them of the offer that had been made to me. If they thought I should accept it, I probably would.

Then, the man from Raleigh who was calling on behalf of the governor dropped a bombshell. He said that if the governor appointed me, he wanted me to sign a legal statement saying that I would vote on that milk commission according to the way that he, the governor, wanted me to vote.

I said, "Well as of now, at nine-thirty at night, my answer would be no. I could never sit on that milk commission and cast one vote at any time that would be detrimental to the dairy producers who had elected me as their president and who depended on me to look out for their welfare. As of now, I would have to say no."

The caller said, "Think it over tonight. I'd like to talk to the governor, and I'll call you back tomorrow."

I thought it over, even though there was nothing to think about because I had already made up my mind. He called me back the next morning at ten o'clock. I told him that I had talked with people in our organization, with our board of directors, and that I could not accept the appointment under the conditions stipulated. I would only accept it if I was completely free to represent the dairy producers and vote as my conscience and my business judgment told me to vote. I could not accept an appointment that had strings tied to it.

I called a meeting of our board of directors for the next day. We met at the Rainbow Inn in Burke County and talked over the situation. They agreed with me that it would never do to accept such an appointment.

Within a month or two, the governor finished his appointments on the milk commission. To fill the position to represent the dairy producers, he appointed a man from the eastern part of the state, whom we had never heard of. He was not a member of our organization, and as far as we knew he was not a member of any other dairy producer organization in the state. He was just an independent producer.

We had lost. We didn't have any representative on the milk commission, anybody who would speak for us. After a month of thinking about it, I called a meeting of our dairy organization's board of directors, and we met in Raleigh. We sat in the Red Lobster, at a private table in a private room, and we talked over our problems for two hours that night. We met again the next morning, when we had asked our legislative representatives to meet with us. Among those representatives was a man from Buncombe County, a man from Haywood County, a man from Henderson County, a man from Mecklenburg County, a man from Burke County, a man from Rutherford County, a man from McDowell County, a man from Mitchell County—at least that many counties; I may have forgotten some.

We met with those men from the legislature, and they told us that they controlled the legislature, as Democrats were still in the majority there. They said for us to get a piece of paper and sit down here and draw up just exactly what we wanted done in relation to the milk commission and the following week they would make it law for us.

After they went back to the General Assembly, we sat down at the Red Lobster cafe and worked out a proposal to abolish the existing North Carolina Milk Commission and to establish a new North Carolina Milk Commission. Within a period of twenty days, that proposal became law, and it became operational, and a new milk commission took effect.

Under the new law, ten people sit on the North Carolina Milk Commission, three appointed by the governor, three appointed by the commissioner of agriculture, and four by the General Assembly. The appointments are made as follows:

> The three members appointed by the Governor shall be two public members and a person who operates a store or other establishment for the sale of fluid milk at retail for consumption off the premises. The two members appointed by the General Assembly upon the recommendation of the President of the Senate shall be a Grade A producer who primarily markets with a cooperative plant and whose primary interest is in operating a dairy farm, and a public member. The two members appointed by the General Assembly upon the recommendation of the Speaker of the House of Representatives shall be a dairy processor-distributor or an employee of a dairy processor-distributor, who primarily operates a proprietary plant, and a public member. The three members appointed by the Commissioner of Agriculture shall be a dairy processor-distributor who primarily operates a cooperative plant and a Grade A producer who primarily markets with a proprietary plant and whose primary interest is operating a dairy farm, and a public member. (North Carolina General Statutes, Volume 15, Chapter 106, Article 28 B, Section 106-266.7)

It was our judgment that the governor should appoint at least three members of that new commission, not a majority, but certainly the three. We felt that way because it was our belief that if we took all of the appointments away, then the news media would come down on us unmercifully. Basically, that was the reason that we felt the three appointments should remain in the hands of our fine governor, Mr. Holshouser. But we took away his right to appoint a producer and a distributor. Under the new law, he appoints a retailer and two members of the consuming public.

We leaned on the shoulders of the commissioner of the North Carolina Department of Agriculture to always appoint a man from a dairy producers organization.

I mentioned earlier that we dairy producers were getting into deep water when we got in the area of planning for and working towards getting a North Carolina Milk Commission. At that time, we did one of the wisest things we had done at all, I guess. We secured an attorney, a well known and capable attorney, to represent us and to meet with us and to guide us from a legal standpoint. The man that we picked for our attorney (and he served us for several years) was Roy Taylor. After he finished his stint as attorney for our dairy producers organization, he became Congressman Roy Taylor from Buncombe County and represented that part of the state in the U.S. Congress for some two or three terms.

Roy Taylor met with us in Raleigh at the Red Lobster cafe and guided us and helped us make decisions about changing that milk commission law. He was at my shoulder when I wrote out in longhand on a legal pad the message that we wanted to give the representatives the next day as to how we wanted the law changed.

This is a long time coming, but I want to pay tribute to that fine lawyer, that fine congressman, that fine gentleman, Roy Taylor.

Incidentally, there is a national forest in western North Carolina called the Roy Taylor National Forest in honor of the fine work he did for his people.

Zeno Ponder

An issue with the pricing of milk came up in June of 1975. This issue came under the jurisdiction of the North Carolina Milk Commission. When the time came for this item to be considered by the commission in a public meeting, open to all, we put out word through our dairy producers organization that we needed to appear in force in Raleigh to present our view on the matter. Members of our organization pretty well filled the meeting room.

A word about the arrangement of those public meetings. They were held in a fairly large room, a room large enough to hold two to three hundred people. Up front, around a curved table, were the nine members of the North Carolina Milk Commission, along with their attorney. Facing them were the seats for the public, the seats that we dairymen occupied.

Notwithstanding that on some days we might be in cow manure up to our ankles, when we dairymen went to a public meeting, that didn't show. We looked everything but that. In fact, we looked pretty sharp. When we went to these public meetings we dressed properly in business suits, white shirts, and ties.

In attending these meetings, and in presenting our viewpoint, we selected in advance the men that we wanted to speak and what we wanted them to say. We presented those men in chronological order, so that each one could build upon what the previous one had said. We laughingly spoke of the men who spoke in public as saying their piece, like school children would say their poems in school. We would laughingly say among ourselves, "Now you be sure you're ready to say your piece. You be sure you do a good job. Don't you mess up on anything."

In our group were some excellent speakers who could handle themselves admirably on the floor, on their feet, with considerable ability. One of the better speakers in our group was the late Mr. Zeno Ponder. He was interested in the dairy business. He was a good dairyman. He was a successful dairyman, but dairy farming was not his number one interest. Mr. Zeno Ponder's number one interest was politics, and politics on the Democratic side of the situation. Mr. Zeno Ponder lived Democratic politics, breathed Democratic politics, and ate Democratic politics. He spent his entire day thinking about politics for the Democratic Party.

When it came time for Mr. Ponder to stand up and present his speech supporting our position before the milk commission, he requested permission from the chairman of the commission to depart a little from the format. Mr. Ponder said, "Mr. Chairman, I have a piece to say. I have some ideas to present on this matter, but before I get into the business part, I want to request your permission to address something else for two or three minutes."

The chairman said, "Mr. Ponder, that will be all right. Go ahead."

Mr. Ponder started off by saying something like this, "It has been my observation for some time and my belief presently that many people in the state of North Carolina have never seen a Republican. It is my belief that most people in this room have never seen a Republican. Now Mr. Chairman, I want to tell you and your members and the other people in this room that today I have here a dyed in the wool Republican. A pure bred, certified Republican. It's going to be my pleasure to present that man. I hope that in doing so, you will not be disappointed."

Mr. Zeno Ponder turned around to the audience and said, "Now, if Mr. A.D. Harrell is here today, I want Mr. Harrell to stand up."

Well, I stood up. I bowed to the front. I bowed to the left. I bowed to the right, and I raised my hands up over my head and gripped them in a universal handshake. The audience was in an uproar of laughter.

I said, "Mr. Ponder, you are doing fine. You have done real good, and I'm proud of you. Now carry on."

Mr. Ponder at that point turned back to the chairman and said, "Mr. Chairman, may I speak for another minute or two?" The chairman granted the request.

Mr. Ponder said, "A month or two ago, I got seriously ill with a bleeding ulcer. I was so ill that I didn't think I was going to live. I don't think my doctors gave me much chance of living. In fact, I was near death. After a few days, the doctors gave me a blood transfusion. They gave me a pint and I felt a little bit better. Two days later, they gave me another pint of blood, and I felt still better. Two days after that they gave me another pint of blood, and I began to improve, gradually but continually."

According to Mr. Zeno Ponder, that sequence went on for a period of about a week or longer. By that time, he had received seven pints of blood. Zeno said after he had those seven pints of blood, he felt like he was about ready to get up and walk, that he was about ready to get some things done. But the doctors wouldn't give their okay to that yet. They wanted him to have one more pint of blood, so he took the eighth pint. According to Mr. Ponder, after he received that eighth pint of blood, he started feeling unusual. He started feeling dizzy. He started feeling real foolish. He couldn't see straight. His thinking was all fuzzy.

Zeno said, "I have never been in such a shape in my life and I didn't know what could possibly be wrong. I called my doctor in and asked him to check back on that eighth pint of blood he had given me. Do you know, gentlemen, that the eighth pint of blood came from a Republican?"

Some five or six years after this episode, I was checking into the Four Seasons Hotel in Greensboro, North Carolina, for a North Carolina Farm Bureau convention. I was standing at the desk, getting my room assignment, when somebody tapped me on the shoulder. It was my good friend Mr. Zeno Ponder. We shook hands and exchanged greetings, then Mr. Ponder said, "I have someone I'd like you to meet, A.D."

I said, "Okay. Bring him on."

He went back into a room somewhere and came back with a lady. He said, "I have remarried, and I want my wife to meet you and for you to meet her."

I met the fine lady, and we exchanged the necessary pleasantries. At the end I asked her, "How long have you known Mr. Zeno Ponder?"

She kind of grinned and said, "I've known him for three years."

I said, "Well, lady, I've known this gentleman for thirty years. In thirty years, I've learned a lot about him. I'm going to give you some advice that will stand you in good stead as long as you are married to this man."

She kind of laughed and said, "What kind of advice is that?"

"Any question that comes up, any controversy, any issue, be it religious, political, community, financial, or whatever—whatever the situation is—before you make any comment, you find out just exactly what position Mr. Ponder is taking. If you'll take the opposite position, you will never be wrong as long as you live."

Mr. Zeno Ponder and I have been good friends down through the years, and whenever we got together, we took time to sit down and laugh and talk about some of these instances that have happened over the years. Mr. Ponder is gone now. He died in 1994. I disagreed with some things he did, but he was my friend, warm, industrious, and intelligent. Bon voyage. May we meet again!

Cleaning Up the Toe River

After I retired as a teacher in the North Carolina school system, I started giving some thought to the possibility of tackling the problem of cleaning up the pollution in the river that drains this entire mountain valley, including the counties of Avery, Mitchell, and Yancey. That river is called the Toe River. During my lifetime, from the time I first saw that river till the time I retired from teaching, it flowed liquid that was the color of chicken soup. It was almost completely white. It smelled bad, it looked bad, and it tasted bad. I felt like I might be able to get enough done to stop that pollution and possibly in my lifetime see that river flow clear and beautiful as it did centuries ago.

To introduce my efforts in the attempt to clean up that river, I want to quote from *The Charlotte Observer* for Thursday, October 11, 1984, from an article written by a gentleman named Tom Higgins, the outdoor writer for the *Observer*. Tom Higgins was raised in Yancey County, so he knew something about this river. Here's what he had to say:

> BURNSVILLE—There's a beautiful, little-visited new river awaiting anglers deep in the Blue Ridge Mountains of Western North Carolina.
>
> Actually, it's a reborn river, abundant with smallmouth bass and muskellunge.
>
> Only God, of course, could create a new river. It is man's task to make them seem new by cleaning up the water after befouling it.
>
> That's what has happened with the Toe River, which forms part of the border between towering Mitchell and Yancey counties before tumbling through a gorge into Tennessee and becoming the Nolichucky.
>
> For most of this century the Toe looked, smelled and was terrible. It was polluted by a variety of plants upstream near Spruce Pine and by raw sewage from practically every home in the watershed. Perhaps worst of all, it became the sludge hole for many mining operations. Through the years, siltation from mica jigs—sites where the soil was washed away from the mineral—poured into the river.

Though 100 yards wide in places, there were few spots where the flow was over ankle deep. A person seemingly could wade the river and, appropriately enough, hardly ever get more than a toe wet.

Then about 15 years ago, a respected Tipton Hill high school educator and coach, A.D. Harrell, upon retiring, turned his energies to reclaiming the Toe.

His crusade coincided with new, wide-spread outrage about pollution. And the Toe, on which man had inflicted such a shameful stubbing, began to be healed.

The salvation of this stream is a happy story for anglers.

Before, the Toe was the color of creamed coffee, and only rough fish species like catfish and some strains of suckers could live in it. As a boy in Yancey County, I seldom heard my father, M.B. Pappy Higgins, then a game warden, cuss. In talking of the Toe and what had been done to it, though, he had vivid verbiage. He remembered a clean, fishable Toe in the early part of the century and the despoiling angered him.

Infirmities prevent Pap, 82, from fishing now, but he's delighted to see the Toe running clear and cold as it did in his youth and providing an almost-perfect habitat for smallmouth and muskies, which have been restored through restocking by the N.C. Wildlife Commission. There's natural reproduction now.

In attempting to clean up the Toe River, we tried to lay a good, workable foundation. The first thing we did was call a group of concerned citizens, citizens who were interested in cleaning up the river. Together, we formed a workable association.

We formed what we called the Toe River Valley Improvement Association. We incorporated the association; we got papers of incorporation from the state, from Raleigh. We engaged an attorney to assist us and advise us.

With the association in place and with an attorney, we were a legal entity, which meant we could receive and dispense funds. It meant we could, if necessary, go to court. The incorporation gave us a standing in court that we wouldn't have had without being incorporated. With that much behind us, we started looking for avenues of approach to attack the problem.

A state committee in Raleigh, North Carolina, that was charged with looking after water pollution and issuing permits for industries to discharge into the streams had a public meeting in Asheville, North Carolina, at what is now the University of North Carolina at Asheville. In the past, it was my understanding, those meetings were attended only by the mining industries in and around Spruce Pine, because they were the ones that had to have the permits to dump things into the river. Other people in general weren't interested in the meetings because they had no financial reason to be there. From a historical standpoint, those public meetings of the Clean Water Committee were not well attended by citizens in general. But, when the announcement of the meeting came out, our group met and decided to send our attorney and me to that meeting to present our viewpoint.

We went to the meeting. My memory says a board of nine gentlemen sat at the head of the auditorium, behind a table with microphones. At one wing of their table was a microphone and a podium set up for public comments, for the public to speak from.

We members of the public signed a paper if we wanted to speak. I signed that paper. When the chairman called my name, I got up from the back of the room where I sat with our attorney to go around the side and behind the gentlemen on the committee to get to the microphone. As I passed behind those gentlemen, I heard the chairman say to the man on his right, "That man looks like he's scared to death." I just made a mental note as I went by. I may have been scared, but I don't know about being *that* scared, though. I went on and made my talk.

From memory, this is approximately what I said: "Here in my lifetime, four of five mining industries in Spruce Pine have polluted the Toe River to the extent that the rest of we people are deprived of any enjoyment of that river in any shape or form. Those mining industries are the Feldspar Corporation, Lawson Mining

Company, International Minerals, and Harris Clay Company. Those are the industries that are dumping silt and mud, all kinds of chemicals used in their manufacturing process, into that river. Because of that, gentlemen, the river has been befouled to the extent that it is unusable.

"I speak for a committee that has been incorporated. We have our attorney, and we are informing you today that we are going to fight and continue to work until this river is cleaned up. No longer will the mining industry be able to put everything from that mining industry into the river without somebody calling their hand.

"Up to this time, we haven't known how to call their hand. We haven't previously been organized; we just didn't know how to get the job done. But I am informing you now, both the committee from Raleigh and the gentlemen that represent those mining industries that I mentioned, that we'll be after you day and night—every day, every night—until that river runs just as clean as it did a hundred years ago.

"I want to emphasize again, gentlemen, that we aren't just talking this time. We have an attorney; we're prepared to act, and we'll be monitoring the river. We have people assigned all up and down the river below the mining industries. Every time that an unusual amount of sludge or color or anything of that nature comes down that river, we're going to try to determine where it came from and get it stopped. Do you have any questions on my comments?"

They did. One member of the committee asked if I owned any property on the river.

"I don't have any property that touches the river. I have property that is fairly close to the river, close enough that I see it practically every day, but I don't have any that actually touches it."

They asked if I was being paid a salary to work on this project.

"No, I'm not. Our committee is funded by local contributions and membership dues, and we use those funds to pay expenses. I pay my travel expenses out of those funds, but as for salary—no."

I thanked them for their time and walked back around the nine gentlemen who were on the committee from Raleigh. As I passed behind the chairman, he turned around and motioned that he wanted to speak to me. I leaned down to see what he wanted. He said, "Mr. Harrell, are you an attorney?"

"No. I'm a farmer. I'm a dairy farmer in Mitchell County. But I do have an attorney with me."

It was interesting, at least from a personal standpoint, that as I went up the man appeared to think, Now here's someone who's scared to death, and as I went back he appeared to think, Maybe he's an attorney and I'd better talk to him.

As I pointed out to the state committee, we had observers up and down the Toe River to monitor the quality of the water. These observers were people who lived close enough to the river till from their residences they could look out on the river and observe what kind of condition the water was in.

In addition to monitoring the quality of the water, we found out how long it took a discharge from the mining companies to reach a particular point on the river. Thereby, we could tell pretty well by mathematical equation the time a discharge had been released.

Let me say something about the permit system that regulated the mining company discharges into the river. In 1982 Congress passed the federal Clean Water Act and put on the states certain responsibilities relative to monitoring and cleaning up some of the discharges into the surface waters all over the country. In North Carolina in response to the Clean Water Act we had a committee that issued permits to the mining companies and to other industries with discharges to surface waters.

Those permits stated what amount of discharge a company could put in the water legally and what they could not put in.

They also required the companies to monitor and keep a log, keep a record, of the discharges that went into that river. They also charged the companies with the responsibility of taking a water sample at a designated time. That water sample had to be turned over to the state Environmental Protection Agency, and they would run tests on that water to see what kind of foreign materials that water was carrying. That was roughly the frame work that was set up to enforce the federal and state Clean Water Acts.

Our problem was that, apparently, when the mining companies got their permits, they went ahead with their operation and, at least at some time, ignored the restrictions in those permits.

For example, one Saturday morning (the mining industries, of course, weren't working that day) one of the monitors on the river called me about eight o'clock. He said, The river this morning is just as white as it can be. Somebody last night has filled it full of mineral discharges somewhere up the river.

The telephone call came from a gentleman in Yancey County. Immediately after taking his call, I called two local game wardens, one from Yancey County and one from Mitchell County. I asked them to meet me at the courthouse door in Bakersville at nine o'clock. Each of them said he would do that.

I was able to get cooperation from those game wardens because over the years I had been a real strong supporter of their programs. I had helped them at numerous times to control poaching and un-lawful hunting and this 'n that, so I had friends in the Wildlife Department. When I asked for help, those two men immediately said they would be there. I wanted them to help because I knew that the mining industries were posted, I knew they had gates and bars at their entrances, I knew they had no trespassing signs posted and this 'n that. I didn't feel free to go inside those gates as a private citizen. Being an officer of the state of North Carolina, a game warden could officially, if he so desired, go inside those gates.

We took one of the game warden's cars, and the three of us started looking at the mining industries. The first one we stopped at was the Feldspar Corporation. Everything looked good; there was no indication of any abnormal discharge at all, so we pulled out and went to the next one upstream. The next one upstream was, I believe, International Minerals. That situation looked all right. We didn't see anything abnormal there.

We got to the Lawson's Mining facility and we found a holding basin of about half an acre. It was so constructed that it was probably about ten feet deep. At the lower end of this holding basin was supposed to be a gate, made out of wood, set in place to hold back the flow of water and so forth from the basin. We found the gate laying on the bank and sludge flowing out of the holding basin into the river. Here was the origin of what the man down the river had seen earlier in the morning.

We took a sample of the sludge in that holding basin. It was of the consistency of thick soup or gravy. We took a sample right out of the basin, put it in a jar, and labeled it. We took a sample of water from the river right above where the discharge was going in, put it into a jar, and labeled it. We took a sample of water from the river right below this discharge, put it into a bottle, and labeled it. We had three samples: one of liquid from the holding basin, one of water above where the discharge was going into the river, and one below, and we took them with us.

We went back to Bakersville and found us a magistrate. In that magistrate's office we swore out depositions of what we had found and what we had seen. We put those depositions in the form of affidavits. We put our names to them and had a notary public notarize them to make them official documents. I thanked the game wardens for their assistance, told them we'd follow up on it, and I'd get back in touch with them.

I took those depositions home with me, wrote a cover letter to them, and mailed them to the U.S. Environmental Protection Agency's office in Atlanta, Georgia, since that was the office that covered our area. We did not send in the water samples. I held them at home.

In a short period of time, in five or ten days, I had an answer from the agency. They acknowledged receipt of our documents and of my letter. In their letter, the Atlanta EPA office said that in response to what they had received they were sending a summons or a warrant to the CEO (chief executive officer) or owner of Lawson Mining Company to appear before a committee in Atlanta at the Federal Building on such and such a date (I don't remember the exact date now) at ten o'clock in the morning. The letter went on to say that they hoped my attorney and I could attend that meeting. I wasn't officially directed to attend that meeting, but they hoped that I would come.

I talked it over with my attorney. He and I decided to go. We drove to the Asheville airport on the designated day, got our tickets, and flew to Atlanta. I had a son working in Atlanta in federal law enforcement at that time; I told him what time we were coming and asked if he could please pick us up. He picked us up at the Atlanta airport and took us to the Federal Building. We arrived in time for the entire EPA hearing.

At the EPA hearing, the owner of Lawson Mining was present with his attorney, my attorney and I were present, and EPA staff members were present. At the beginning of the meeting, the EPA official in charge had his attorney read the three affidavits from the two wardens and me. The company owner was asked if he had any questions about those affidavits. He didn't. He was asked if in his opinion those affidavits stated the facts as he knew them to be about his company's operation. He said he didn't know if they were correct or if they were incorrect; he just didn't know that

much about the discharge that went into the river from the company. He would admit that the discharge went in as stated in the
affidavits, but that was all he knew about it.

From the work we had done prior to this meeting, we had been
able to ascertain that the discharge was released on Friday night at
approximately eleven-thirty. We figured that out by going down
river to a point where the discharge had not yet arrived and waiting for it to get there, then recording the time of day. We knew
how far it was back up to Lawson Mining Company, and with our
formula we calculated the time of discharge, that is the time we
think the gate was opened up and the contents of this holding basin were allowed to flow into the river.

The owner said that this time might well be right. He said in fact
he had never been down to the gate and he didn't know which
employees opened it or what time they opened it.

The EPA officials said that they would discuss this information
and that each of us would receive notification. Sometime later on I
received a photostated copy of the findings of the committee there
in Atlanta. They found the facts to be as we had presented them in
our affidavits. They found as a fact that the company owner had
not properly monitored the discharges from his mining operation,
and he was told that any further illegal discharge would bring
criminal action on the part of EPA. This pretty well ended that matter as I recall.

Getting the river cleaned up wasn't a project that reaped re-
wards immediately. It was a long-term situation. We made improvements gradually, slowly, one at a time. Of course each mining
company had to have time to make whatever arrangements were
necessary not to violate their discharge permits. I suppose that
each of them had maybe a year to make whatever changes in their

operations that were necessary to comply with the Clean Water Act. Over a period of years, the mining industry ceased to put into the river things that had damaged it for fifty or seventy-five years.

Since our efforts at cleaning up the river, the mining industry has hauled their sludge and tailings and refuse from their operations away from the river and hauled it back on land they own and have dumped it in previously mined areas. They have done a marvelous job. They have seeded that land in grass and set it with trees and have fertilized and limed it so that vegetation would grow. Now, instead of all the sand, silt, and discoloration going to the Toe River, it is a beautiful scene of reclaimed land.

The mining industry has done a marvelous job beautifying the area, in cleaning up what was an intolerable mess. For that, the mining industry of Mitchell County is due a big thanks from all the people of the county. They have turned their act around and produced something now of beauty, instead of the mess going down that river. No longer do mothers with young children along that river have to be real careful and ever vigilant to see that those young children don't wade or swim in muddy, filthy, nasty water.

It should be pointed out that aside from the river pollution, the Spruce Pine mining industries did much good for the county. They were fine corporate citizens. They provided many jobs for our local people. They paid good wages. They treated their employees well. They were in effect the economic backbone of Spruce Pine for the first half of this century. They have done many things for Mitchell County that might not have been done otherwise without them. Any criticism of their pollution problems should be balanced with the much good that they have done.

CHAPTER SEVEN

Farm Life

How Hard Is a Diamond?

My father passed down to me, and I'm sure his father passed to him, knowledge about certain types of night that are important to we who live in the world of agriculture.

The first of those nights that my father told me about is what he called the "sheep-killing night." That was a night in which the weather consisted of gentle but continuous rain, rather warm rain, with every indication that it wasn't going to quit raining before daylight, just going to rain all night and maybe into the next day, too. My father said that was the type of night that the dogs which were allowed to run free in the neighborhood and the wild dogs and the stray dogs would get together in a pack and kill the farmer's sheep. I recall that my father lost ninety-seven sheep in one of those sheep-killing nights. (The raising of sheep is no longer as important in this area as it once was. The number of sheep lost to dogs plus the ill feelings that developed when farmers killed the dogs caused farmers to stop raising sheep.)

The second type of night my father told me about is what he called the "witches enhance night." That was a night when the weather was so bad that no human being would dare of his own volition be out in the weather in an automobile or any other wise. Those were nights when the rain wasn't falling straight down; it was falling practically horizontal, with a little ice or sleet mixed in.

Those were the nights when he said the only thing that would be out was a witch or a haint.

The third type of night, and it's the one that's important to this story, is the warm summer night when the ground is moist and the temperature is up to about seventy or seventy-five degrees and everybody's lawn and everybody's garden and everybody's crops are growing so as to be bursting at the seams. Everything is really growing. After that type of night, the common greeting between neighbors the next morning would be, "Boy, the gardens grew last night, didn't they? My garden looks so good, the corn looks good, the tobacco looks good. Everything is really growing." That is the type of night that we are dealing with here.

One night late in the month of June, my telephone rang about twelve-thirty, and I turned over and fumbled around, half awake and half asleep, and finally found the telephone. I was just awake enough to know that telephones ringing that time of night do not usually bring any particular good news.

The voice on the other end of the telephone said, "This is the county sheriff's office. A car on patrol in your area reports that below your house and barn, almost in front of your home, the road is filled with cattle. Some twenty-five or thirty or forty head of cattle. Those cattle are moving down Harrell Hill Road toward North Carolina Highway Two-Twenty-Six."

I told the sheriff's department that I would take care of that. I woke Geneva and told her she would have to drive me down till we got in front of those cattle. Then, I would drive them back home and she could drive along behind me and give any assistance as needed.

We dressed and got in a vehicle and drove down to Highway 226. About halfway down, we saw signs of where the cattle had been in the road, where they had left droppings and so forth. Then, we ran out of any signs of cattle. We couldn't find them.

We came back home. I called central dispatching at the sheriff's department and asked them to please radio that car that gave the report about the cattle being out and see if they could find out where the cattle went to. The dispatcher said, "Just stand by the telephone; it won't take but a minute."

In a short time the sheriff's department called back and said, "Our patrol car says the cattle turned off the left of the road, down near a Mr. Dow's trailer, and went up beside his trailer into the fields." I thanked the caller.

Geneva and I drove back down there. With a flashlight, I found the tracks of the cattle where they had gone from the road and up by the man's trailer, right through the man's fine, growing garden. The garden was about halfway mature, I'd say.

What surprised me was that the cattle hadn't stopped to eat that garden. They could have eaten it up in about two minutes, but they hadn't stopped, which meant they were scared by something. (I later found out that the cattle had gotten in front of the patrol car. This car was driven by a man who didn't understand cattle. He had tried to run by them, and had scared them to death, so they stampeded down the highway and through the garden. That was the reason they hadn't stopped to eat up the man's garden.)

I noticed which direction the cattle had gone. They had gone into the woods to the left of the garden. In that area of woods there is a hundred acres. The cattle might come out by daylight or they might not come out by daylight. I went back to where Geneva was sitting in the car.

By then it was about two o'clock in the morning. I said to her, "You go on back to the house and go to bed. Get some rest if you can. When it gets daylight, you come back down here. I'll sit here beside this man's garden and see that those cattle don't get in that garden. If they come down, I'll do what I have to do to keep them out. You come back at daylight and help me."

I found me a big rock fairly close to the man's garden and I sat down on that rock. I sat down on that rock about five minutes after two. By two-thirty, that rock got pretty hard. It crossed my mind, that diamond is the hardest substance known to man. It crossed my sleepy mind that people who think a diamond is so hard have never sat on a flint rock at five after two in the morning. If they had, they might have changed their minds.

A lot of things went through my mind. I had to stay awake, of course. In that number of hours, it being dark and everybody asleep and everybody quiet, all kinds of things go through a man's mind. Here's one thing that went through my mind a half a dozen times while I was sitting on that hard rock.

I thought, "Well now, I spend my hours, when I have free hours, grouse hunting and doing such things as that. My brother, Bruce, spends his spare time building fences."

Bruce has about the same number of cattle that we have, but he has his cattle behind a five- or six-strand barbed wire fence. It's just a super fence, built with steel posts. We have our forty or fifty head of cattle behind one single strand of fence that has electric current on it, an electric fence. There's not much between our cattle and the highway to keep them from getting out. Sometimes a deer runs over that electric fence and tears it down, so I assumed that had probably happened this night.

I thought to myself, "If I were to have quit grouse hunting and some of the other foolish things I do and spent the time building good fences, I wouldn't be sitting here."

Be that as it may, I sat there until about daylight. When it got to be daylight enough to move around through the woods, to track down where they were, I took off through the woods and found the herd of cattle. I got around them and drove them back out through the woods, down by the man's garden, to the highway. Geneva had come on down and had parked so that when the

View of some of Bruce Herrell's pasture land, looking northeast from the Pleasant Grove Church of the Brethren. Roan Mountain is in the background.

cattle came out they had to go on up our way instead of in a different direction. I got this herd of cattle to the highway and went and spoke a word or two to Geneva, then looked over that bunch of cattle.

"Geneva!" I said. "These are not our cattle. These are Bruce's cattle. That's his bull, his big two-thousand-pound bull. Those are his cows, and those are his calves. I was sitting down here all night guarding *his* cattle!

"You get in the car and go on up there to Bruce's. If he's not up, tell him to get out of that bed and get down here and help me."

In about twenty minutes, here came Bruce and his family and Geneva, and we rounded up his cattle and drove them back up the road and put them in his pasture. There, I found out what had happened. That big bull of his had decided that the grass was greener on the other side of the fence and that he was going through the fence. That big bull had marched right through that five-strand barbed wire fence, had bent over the steel posts, and had torn the whole fence down. All of the cattle had gone through that open space, down the gravel road from the pasture, to the highway by our place. About that time, the man from the sheriff's department had come by and had assumed that the cattle belonged to me. But they didn't.

Bruce and I had a big laugh. He was in bed asleep, and I was out sitting on a rock that I would have bet any man was harder than a diamond. But things even up over time. I have played tricks on him, and that one came back on me.

Bruce's Cattle Kick Down the Barn Door

My brother, Bruce, keeps beef cattle on his farm, as do my family and I, on our farm. Really, Bruce is a better herdsman than I am. He takes a little more care of his cattle, he's a little more careful with them, and he looks after them a little bit more than I do. For example, in the winter time, I'll leave gates and barn doors open where our herd of cattle can come to the barn at their own volition. They can come in out of the weather when they want to, and they can lay out on the hillside when they want to. I leave it up to them entirely.

Incidentally, there are only two or three types of weather that will cause cattle to come in off the hills into a covered barn. The cattle will stay out on the hillside in cold weather. But in driving snow or heavy rain, or heavy wind without snow or rain, the cattle will come to the barn. They'll stay in that barn, in the dry, in the shelter, until the weather changes, then they'll go back out. So, I leave it up to our cattle to make up their own minds as to whether they want to stay out on the hills or whether they want to come to the barn, if there's any possibility of foul weather.

One fine December evening, my grouse hunting route took me on a situation where I was coming back by the barn where Bruce was putting up his cattle. This was about an hour before dark on a winter's evening. As I approached the vicinity where Bruce's cattle were, I saw about twenty head of young animals. By "young animals" I mean cattle around a year old. There were some twenty head of young animals in the field around Bruce's barn. I was on the ridge line, in the woods, where I could see the barn and cattle, and see and hear Bruce, and know what was going on. As I came down the ridge line heading toward our house, I heard Bruce rounding up the cattle and moving them along into the barn.

He was saying, "Go along. Hey. Move on. Let's go. Come on. Get in there. You need to be in there out of the weather. You need to be in there tonight. It'll be warmer in there than it will out here. Move on. Go along. Move along. . . ," the normal things that a cattle driver will say to his cattle. The cattle understand it. Some people don't.

I heard him move the cattle into the barn, and I heard him close the doors. Now we just don't put real strong doors on our barns. We normally close those doors with a latch, a slat of wood about an inch thick, four inches wide, and three or four feet long, and drop that latch into some sort of device to hold the doors closed.

About the time Bruce got his cattle in the barn and closed the doors and dropped the slat into the device to keep the doors closed, my dog pointed a grouse. The dog and I were maybe a hundred and ten yards from the barn. I walked up behind the dog and flushed the grouse out. It flew straight away, and I shot, but I missed the bird.

When I shot, I heard a lot of commotion from that barn where Bruce and those calves were. Clearly, my shot had disturbed those calves a great deal. In fact, it sounded like they were about to break out of there.

Bruce is a mild-spoken man, no profanity. But he had some things to say about his cattle being scared, about somebody up there in those woods shooting around, scaring his cattle when he should be doing something else. Bruce didn't think much of that.

The cattle kind of settled down, and I heard Bruce go to his feed bin and get feed and put it in the feed manger for the cattle, talking to them in a calm, gentle voice, trying to settle them down.

My dog and I went on, maybe two hundred yards away from that barn, when the dog found that bird again and pointed. I walked up behind the dog, flushed the bird. The bird flew around in a semi-circle, not a real good target. I shot, and the bird turned around to the left, giving me a little better target, and I shot again.

Those two shots came within a space of about two seconds. When I fired that second shot, it sounded like those calves stampeded. I heard the sticks that were used to close the barn door break. I heard the barn doors crash open, and I heard those calves come out of there, scared to death. Right up the valley they went, where Bruce had spent half an hour or forty-five minutes herding them out of. They went right back up in there.

Bruce came out of the barn. I couldn't help but listen. The wording he put on whoever it was up there in the woods, shooting and scaring his calves half to death, I shouldn't put on this page.

I sniggered a little bit. Although my way home was right down by that barn, right down by Bruce and those calves, I decided I had better not go that way. I peeled off on the other side of the ridge and went down the other valley, east of where the barn was, about twenty minutes out of my way. I came down the other valley and finally hit the highway some distance below my house and walked back up the highway to my house.

I put my dog up, put my gun up, and got in my vehicle. I thought I had better go back up there and help Bruce put those cattle up. When I got back up there, he asked something about what I was doing.

I said, "Well, I'm just going up here to check on things a little bit. I thought to see if you needed any help, to see if Aunt May is all right, and this 'n that."

"Have you been grouse hunting today?"

"Who, me? Grouse hunting? It's been some time since I've been grouse hunting. I just don't know how long it has been since I've been grouse hunting. It's been some time. In fact, it may have been some thirty or forty-five minutes since I've been grouse hunting."

"I knew that was you all the time!"

Horse Cow

In our group of dairy cows, our registered Guernsey cows, was a special cow or two. All of those Guernsey cows are real gentle. They are real responsive to kindness and good treatment. They tolerate a lot of children's playing and this n' that. One of those cows was so gentle that the younger children, when they went after the cows, would get on her back and would ride her to the house or to the milking parlor. They affectionately called her the "Horse Cow" and looked forward to bringing the cows in.

When it was evident that the Horse Cow was in labor, we put her into the maternity stall, where we had lights, where we could look after her and care for her and the calf. After four hours, it was clear to us that something was wrong. The normal delivery time for a cow to have her calf is from three to four hours. When we checked on this cow four hours after she had been in labor, she hadn't made any progress in delivering the calf and she was losing entirely too much blood. Losing blood is completely unusual for cows; they should lose hardly any blood in a normal calf delivery.

It was midnight at this stage, and the Horse Cow had lain down and was suffering. Geneva and I decided that we had to do what we could to help her deliver the calf. That was nothing unusual. We had helped deliver calves in many, many difficult calvings, and we had never lost a cow and we had hardly ever lost a calf. We were pretty proficient in assisting the animal, in knowing what to do and what not to do.

In this case, the blood loss concerned us considerably. We decided that she could not afford to lose blood very long at that rate. I put on a shoulder-length glove and took a soft rope and went inside the birth canal and tied that rope around the calf's nose and two front feet, which come out first. I tied the rope in place, and Geneva and I together under the lights pulled with the necessary pressure, and we delivered that calf.

When we pulled that calf out, to our dismay, we saw it was normal from its nose and head and front feet and shoulders—normal skin, hair, and everything—but from midway to the backbone back, there was no skin on the animal, no skin at all. In delivery, the uncovered short ribs of that calf had acted as a knife and had lacerated the tissues of the Horse Cow, and she was bleeding.

As soon as we pulled the poor, deformed calf out, the Horse Cow bled profusely. We couldn't do anything. We sat there beside her and watched for some ten or fifteen minutes, until she died from loss of blood.

You have to have been in an agricultural economy and to have handled animals and to have loved animals to really appreciate our feelings of loss as we closed the stall door and put our arms around each other and walked back to the house that night. As we walked that fifty yards, each of us had tears streaming down our cheeks. We went inside the house, undressed, and went to bed. A half hour later, I reached over and touched Geneva and realized that she was still crying.

You win some and you lose some, but you do the best you can.

We Leave the Dairy Business

In the late 1970s, the price of dairy cattle went real high. The price of a thirteen hundred- or fourteen hundred-pound dairy cow would run in the range of $1200 to $1500 each. At that time, Geneva and I began to look at the possibility of closing down the dairy and cashing in with our cows and taking life a little bit easier. Our children were out of school, and we didn't have the financial burden and responsibility that we had when those children were growing up and going to school and going to university.

It was in 1980, in a private treaty, that we sold our dairy herd. A tractor-trailer rig, with a trailer big enough to hold forty or fifty animals, backed into the loading chute at our dairy farm. We loaded the animals and took our money and put it in the bank.

It's interesting to note that the interest on this money in some months was more than the profit from our milking operation. Be that as it may, we closed down the dairy operation and used our energies and time in other things.

Although we were out of the dairy business, we still had, and I suppose always will have, a warm feeling in our hearts for those fine dairy cows we ran on the farm. Also, frequently, we run into some of the members of the dairy organization that we worked for. Whenever we do, it is a big pleasure to sit down and visit with those men. I don't think a summer ever passes that we don't run into some of the members of the board of directors as we move about western North Carolina. These meetings always have a lot of warm, glad-to-see-you feelings.

We have a son who works in federal law enforcement in Charlotte, in Mecklenburg County. I have told this son, "You find time to go by the farm of Mr. Irving Cook. Visit with him, tell him who you are, and that your daddy asked you to come by and speak with him."

Mr. Cook lived at Huntersville, which is a suburb of Charlotte. He represented Mecklenburg County in our dairy organization in the years we were in the dairy business, and he was an important member of the board of directors, and eventually became president of the organization. I wanted him and our son to meet.

Velmer Bennett's Cows

A friend of mine named Velmer Bennett, a young man who had worked on the farm here for me at various times over the years, came to me the first of May and said, "A.D., I've got eighteen head of beef cattle down at my dad's. Those cattle have eaten up the pasture, they have gotten out on a neighbor's lands, and I'm having trouble with them. I can't do a thing with them. I noticed that you don't have any cattle up on your property over at Tipton Hill. Is there any chance you would let me take those eighteen head of cattle and put them on your property at Tipton Hill and let them pasture there over the summer?"

"Velmer, that will be fine if you put them in there," I said.

He wanted to know what I would charge him for pasturing them during the summer.

"I won't charge you anything. You'll probably have to work on the fence some because I haven't had any cattle in there in a year or two and the fence might need repair. You go on and repair the fence and keep a record of any posts or wire or anything you buy to fix that fence, because the fence will do me some good after you move your cattle. You go ahead and put your cattle in there, and leave them over the summer. That will be fine. I won't charge you anything at all.

"But one thing I do want now. I want you to move those cattle by Thanksgiving. Come Thanksgiving day, I want those cattle out of there. I don't want them running in those fields in the winter time. So, by Thanksgiving day I want you to move them or do something with them."

He said, "I'll do that. That won't be any problem at all. I'll sell them or do something with them by Thanksgiving."

Summer went along. Velmer worked on the fence and fixed it up. He brought me a bill, and I paid for whatever he had to buy to fix the fence. His cattle did well. He was pleased with the whole situation.

Come a day or two before Thanksgiving, Velmer came over to my house. He said, "A.D., I can't get those cattle out of there. I got my girl friend, my brother, two of his boys, and two brothers of my girl friend. We went over there and spent half a day trying to get those cattle out of there. They were scared to death. They ran to the woods as far as they could get away, and we just couldn't get them out. I don't know what to do. I don't believe I can get them out by Thanksgiving."

"Well, just get them out as soon as you can. We'll get along with it all right."

"Next Saturday," said Velmer. "I don't work next Saturday and I'll get my crowd together again. We'll go over there and we'll get those cattle out."

The next Saturday came, and Velmer Bennett came to my house late in the evening, all flustered and tired and worn out. He said, "We have chased those cattle for three hours and we can't get them out of that pasture. I've got next Saturday off and I'll bring the same crew back and I'll pick up four or five other people. I'll get enough people around those cattle till I can get them out of there and I'll take them home."

I said, "Okay."

The next Saturday evening he came to me again with the same story. "We've tried and we've tried and we've tried. Those cattle

are absolutely scared to death of us. We can just go inside the field
and they'll leave. They'll put their tails up on their backs and run
just as hard as they can run. We might as well try to get deer out of
there as to try and get those cattle out of there. We can't do a thing
with them."

I said, "Well, just let them go. When it gets cold, feed them and
do what you have to do to take care of them."

The cattle stayed in there until after Christmas. At Christmas
time I ran into Velmer and we talked about the cattle situation, that
he couldn't get them out.

The fact is that if strangers go in a pasture where cattle are, those
cattle will realize they're strangers and get upset. Those cattle will
run just like they are scared to death and they'll stampede. You
can't do a thing with cattle when they stampede. The more Velmer
tried to get them out, the more people he got together to get them
out, the more scared the cattle got so that he couldn't do a thing
with them.

"Velmer," I said, "I don't know but one thing to do, and that's for
me just to buy those cattle then I'll get them out or do something
with them."

"Would you buy them?"

"Yeah. I'll buy them. Looks like the only way to get rid of them,
to get them out of the area."

We agreed on a price, and I paid him for them. Of course I
wanted to bring them to our farm here, where we live, where our
other cattle were, so I could feed them without too much trouble. I
didn't want to feed cattle here then drive to Tipton Hill and feed
that eighteen head.

"How are you going to get them out?" Velmer asked,

"I don't think I'll have any problem at all about getting them
out. Next Monday morning I want you and your girlfriend—no
more; don't bring anybody else with you—to go over there in your
car and watch me get those cattle out of there."

"A.D., it can't be done!"

"Well, give me a try. Now don't you feed those cattle anything. Let me take care of the whole thing. Just get there at ten o'clock."

At nine-thirty I put a bale of hay in my truck and went over to the gate where the cattle would come out. Velmer and his girl-friend were sitting in the car. He asked what I wanted them to do.

I said, "Back your car down the road here about fifty yards. Roll your windows down. Don't say a word. Just watch what goes on."

I took some hay under each arm and I walked out to where the cattle had been being fed. I spoke to them in a low voice. That low voice is real important; if you speak to them in a high voice, a shrill voice, they get upset immediately. I spoke to them in a low voice and said something like, "Here's a bite of hay. Come on."

I laid down enough hay for one or two of them to get a bite or two. I threw a little more hay out toward the gate. I got to the gate and opened it. Outside the gate, on the road, I laid down two or three more bites of hay. I moved my truck on up the road apiece, out of the way, and put a little more hay down behind the truck. By that time all of the eighteen head of cattle were out of the pasture and were eating hay on the road. I moved around behind them and closed the gate.

I went down to Velmer's car and said to him, "I'm going to go in front of the cattle with my truck. I'll leave a little hay on the tail-gate, where they'll see it. I'll drive real slow, and they'll tend to fol-low that truck. What I want you to do is just to drive in your car about twenty-five to thirty yards behind the cattle. I think I'll take them right straight to my house without any trouble."

Within thirty-five minutes, I opened the gate on my farm at home and turned the eighteen head of cattle in. Velmer drove up shaking his head. "Well, that's the biggest surprise I've ever had in my life," he said.

Mr. McKinney's Hay

Just west of the Brethren church on Harrell Hill are some fields of grass land. These fields run from the highway in front of the church northward to the head of the hollow. Historically, these fields have been used to grow grass or hay that is harvested in the summertime, usually the first of June, then stored in barns to feed cattle during the winter. Twenty to twenty-five years ago, those fields were divided into two sections. The section next to the highway belonged to Mr. Tipton. The northernmost section of those fields was owned by Mr. McKinney.

Mr. Tipton worked out a deal with my boys and me to rake and bale his hay and to put it in a barn. We didn't mow the hay; some other neighbor mowed the hay, but we were going to help Mr. Tipton by putting the hay in the barn. We took to his field two tractors, a hay rake, a hay baler, and two trucks to haul the hay from the field to the barn. We had some hired help to drive the trucks. My sons and I were doing the hay raking and baling.

Along in the afternoon, about five o'clock, we finished Mr. Tipton's hay. We had raked and bailed the entire field and put the hay in his barn. Just across the fence from Mr. Tipton's field was the field owned by Mr. McKinney. The same man who mowed Mr. Tipton's hay had mowed Mr. McKinney's. On the same day that Mr. Tipton's hay was ready for the barn, Mr. McKinney's hay was ready for the barn, but Mr. McKinney had not spoken to us about his hay. Mr. McKinney wasn't there. Mr. McKinney was a big man, six foot four, industrious, a good man, but he wasn't there to look after his hay and it needed attention.

When we finished Mr. Tipton's hay, I said, "Gentlemen, you may not know it, but Mr. McKinney is not here because his wife is terminally ill at the medical center in Johnson City and he's down there with her. In my opinion, it just won't do for us to leave this area, take these trucks and equipment out, with this hay here and nobody to look after it."

We opened his gate, drove our equipment in his field and went to work. By seven or eight o'clock that night, certainly before dark, we had finished Mr. McKinney's hay. We had raked it and baled it and put it in his barn at the lower side of his field.

After we finished but before we moved our equipment out of the area, Mr. McKinney drove up in his pickup truck. He got out, looked over the field; it was clean and everything was in good order for him.

He turned his back to us. He stood with his back turned toward us for ten or maybe fifteen seconds. Then he turned around and looked at us, his eyes completely filled with tears, and said, "Thank you, pard."

Mr. McKinney is now long gone, but whenever I see his children today, particularly the boys, they mention the fact that I put up the hay when their mother was in the hospital. Those children and Mr. McKinney used to go to our Brethren church. The children have left the community, and I only see them infrequently now. But when we do meet, those boys of his express a thank you. All of my life I will remember the term "thank you, pard."

CHAPTER EIGHT

Perfect Hunting Days
and Other Blessings

A Perfect Hunting Day with Doug

There are some perfect days in every endeavor. There are some days that are indelibly imprinted on our memories. I want to pass on to the reader some of those episodes I have been involved in, in my sixty years of grouse hunting.

In addition to grouse hunting, there are some other blessings to be enjoyed on this planet. One of the greatest blessings is that blessing that comes from having good neighbors. My family and I have enjoyed, we have loved, and we have rubbed shoulders with some of the best neighbors that one can imagine.

The Lester Miller family is near to the top of the list of the good neighbors. The Lester Miller family consists of two girls and five boys, all of whom are outstanding and splendid individuals.

Lester and I have known each other all of our lives. We went to elementary school together. We stayed in touch through the years. Now that each of us is in the last quarter of our four score and ten years, we are still the best of friends and help each other in every way that we can. When I leave this area and go off on hunting trips for two or three weeks, either Lester or one of the boys drives by my place each day, by our cattle pastures, just to see that everything is okay. With them to depend on, I have no worry about things back home when I'm in Wisconsin or Minnesota or Michigan, or wherever.

Some years ago, Lester stopped by my house and said, "A.D., the boys and I were coon hunting a night or two ago up on Roan Mountain. In that two or three hours of coon hunting, we must have had ten or fifteen grouse flushes as we tromped around through the woods, following our dogs and so forth. I wanted to stop by and tell you where those grouse were, and maybe you and your boys could find them and enjoy an evening of hunting."

Well, that's typical of Lester.

A few days later, my son, Doug, and I took an English setter named Sam and we went to the area that Lester had told me about. In just a few minutes the English setter found birds and pointed. Doug and I moved up on either side of the dog. I don't remember exactly how many birds flushed, some two or three or maybe four.

When Doug and I hunt together, we automatically go in, me on the left and Doug on the right side. When the birds flushed, I shot and one fell. I heard Doug shoot a time or two, and I turned and asked how he did.

He said, "I've got two birds down over here."

In a period of a few minutes, the dog brought all three birds in. We patted the dog on the head and told him how fine he was and proceeded on up the valley.

It wasn't long before we had another point that was productive. A bird or two flushed, and I killed that bird, I believe.

A little later on, another point, more birds flushed, and Doug fired again and got another bird. That was three for Doug and two for me. The possession limit in North Carolina is three birds per man. When we are hunting with two men out, we say the limit is six birds per two men.

I said, "Doug, you give me one of your birds, and that'll make my possession limit out. If other birds flush, you'll have some more shooting to do."

A.D. Harrell with grouse and Doug Harrell with Tom Dooley Dog,
a Brittany, in 1978.

We went on the afternoon another hour or two and found more birds. Doug killed another one, which made him really a total of four birds and myself two. Since I was carrying one of his birds, we had the legal possession limit of six birds for a two-man party.

In that two or three hours of hunting, we had perfect dog work. The shooting wasn't perfect, but it was reasonably good, good enough till we had six birds after a three-hour hunt. That's not a bad afternoon for a father and a son.

That is one of the episodes that I consider a perfect day. My partner had a fine time. Everything fell in place, and we came off the mountain about as happy as two hunters could be.

Geneva Harrell holding a woodcock (left) and a grouse (right) in Wisconsin. Seven more grouse are lying on the cushion. (We told you she's great shot!)

Perfect Hunting Days with Geneva

Any recounting of perfect hunting days would be incomplete unless that list included some perfect days with my wife, Geneva. Frequently in years past when I went going on short hunting trips (this would have been years ago, because we've both reached ages of seventy now and our hunting trips together now are few and far between) she would go with me. She has a model eleven hundred, twenty-gauge gun she can shoot real well.

One day we went into the Pisgah National Forest and hunted some three or four hours. I had killed, I believe, a bird or two. As we came back out, driving down the rough road, a grouse flew from the right across the road, in front of us, and lit over on the left of the road. Each of us saw the bird; it lit some thirty yards above the bank of the road.

I stopped immediately, and Geneva got out. While she got out, I loaded her gun and handed it to her. She stepped around in front of the truck. The bird flushed.

It could have flown half a dozen ways and been safe, but it came back across the road pretty much in front of her. Geneva put up her twenty-gauge gun and pulled the trigger and that grouse fell.

We watched it fall and when it fell we saw water splash. It had fallen in a stream a few yards below the road, a sizeable stream. We went down to the banks of the stream to get the bird and couldn't find it.

We went back to the truck and turned the dog loose. The dog and us together couldn't find it. We started going down the stream, looking. We walked some two hundred yards down that stream and saw the bird over in the middle of the stream, where it lay on a sand bar. We were able to retrieve that bird.

Another such perfect day in which Geneva happened to be involved happened in Wisconsin. We were hunting in Chequamegon National Forest. One afternoon, Geneva went with Rusty and me, while Doug and his wife hunted with Tim in another area.

Geneva and I, going out on a logging road, found Rusty on point. We walked up to him. Geneva stopped when we got to the dog, which put her on the dog's left. I moved on around behind the dog and put myself on the dog's right. I glanced over at Geneva and she nodded that she was ready. Everything looked good, so I flushed the birds.

When the birds flushed, I believe there were four or five of them, two of them came around on my quadrant of what we were looking at. I fired a time or two and at least one of those birds fell.

I didn't take my gun down from my shoulder. Instead, I swung my gun back to the left in the direction of the birds in front of Geneva. As I swung around I saw out of the corner of my eye a bird falling. Geneva had already killed one.

We, in a period of a few minutes there, picked up two birds, one that I had killed and one that she killed.

Those situations happened to us, fortunately, several times when we were years younger than we are at the present time.

After this incident, when we went back to the truck, I took my big map out that I had of Chequamegon National Forest, and I located the road in which Geneva had killed a bird and I had killed a bird. On that road we put in ink "Geneva Road." When we got back to camp, we went to all of our maps and put the same notation on all of them and named that road for Geneva.

In the years since that time, I have gone back to that location each time we go to Wisconsin. It has pretty well changed from what it was when Geneva and I killed the two birds. The Forest Service has dug a huge gravel pit in that area, and the exact location in which Geneva and I were standing has been pretty well eliminated, but we still check the area each time that we go back to the state of Wisconsin.

Ruffed Grouse and Grandsons

A Northwest Airlines jet, flying in light snow, comes to a halt at the airport in Iron City, Michigan, on October 15, 1990. On the tar-

A.D. and Greg Harrell; Western Carolina University
military ball, 1993.

mac stand two men in grouse-hunting garb, intently watching the
passengers deplane.

There he is! A tall handsome young man with a military haircut
comes down the unloading chute. He spots the two waiting hunters, flashes a coast-to-coast smile, and calls out, "Hi, Dad. Hi,
Daddy Dee. This is some snow storm. The sun was shining in
North Carolina."

Thus starts a pleasure-filled week in which a seventy-five-year-
old grandfather enthusiastically teaches an eighteen-year-old
grandson (and a fine grandson he is!) the fine points of hunting
the ruffed grouse in the North Woods of Michigan and Wisconsin.

Now it is impossible for anyone, in one week, to absorb all the
grouse hunting information that this grandfather, Daddy Dee, has
accumulated in a lifetime, but the two men, the young man and
the old man, had a ball. They didn't kill a lot of grouse but there
was a bonding between the two men, based on love, appreciation,
and respect, that will last long after the old man is gone. "God is in

Two future grouse hunters: Adam Harrell,
thirteen years old, and Jesse Harrell, two years
old.

His heaven and all is right with the world" when a grandson and a
grandfather hunt behind the super Brittany we used that week.

The grandson is Greg Harrell, son of Doug and Barbara Harrell.
The grandfather is A.D. Harrell. The Brittany is three-year-old
Dottie.

Greg is a student at Western Carolina University. With the blessings of his girlfriend, he has flown to Minneapolis-Saint Paul and
then on to Iron City, Michigan, where we have picked him up in
our hunting vehicle. This is the second week of our 1990 hunting
trip. Due to National Guard maneuvers, Greg couldn't make the
first week of hunting.

This is the twenty-first consecutive year that the Harrells have
vacationed and hunted grouse in the Wisconsin and Michigan
North Country. Another fine grandson, Tony, older than Greg,

brightened a wonderful week for me in 1985. Yet another grand-son, Adam, is waiting his turn.

One of my many prayers is, "Keep me strong and healthy till ten-year-old Adam reaches his sixteenth birthday." A hunting pair made up of a sixteen-year-old grandson and an eighty-one-year-old grandfather would be a picture that would warm the heart.

I do have faith.

HONOR ROLL OF HUNTING PARTNERS

Here are the names of those fine outdoorsmen who have hunted grouse with me. The men who have climbed these mountainsides with me, who have walked the drag trails, crawled through the laurel hells, and dropped over a ridge line into the next valley.

Scott Beasley
George Blevins
Steve Blevins
Larry Boone
John Collins
Phil Dale
Oscar Deyton
Walton Gooden
Roy Gore
Jerry Gouge
Dr. Ben Hall
Dave Hamby
J. J. Hamlin
Doug Harrell
Larry Harrell
Charles Hill
Tom Hood
Ed Jones
Hobart Miller
James Miller
Mike Mills
Warren Parker
Edward Proffitt
Bob Rowe

ACKNOWLEDGMENTS

Many thanks to Susan Norris, who transcribed and edited the audiotapes that I recorded for this book. Many thanks also to Diana Donovan of Celo Valley Books, who designed the cover, advised on design and typography, finalized the typography, and guided the book through printing and binding.

The following publications have graciously granted permission to reprint material: the *Asheville-Citizen Times*, for the quotation from John Parris in chapter one ("Roaming the Mountains" by John Parris. Copyright © 1995 by the *Asheville Citizen-Times*.), and *The Charlotte Observer*, for the long quotation from Tom Higgins in chapter six ("Fishing Is Good Again in a Clean Toe River" by Tom Higgins. Copyright © 1984 by *The Charlotte Observer*.).

Unless otherwise noted, all photographs were taken by Harrell family members and friends.